TALES OF THE SCOTTISH CLANS

ROB ROY IN HIDING

Frontispiece

TALES OF THE SCOTTISH CLANS

BY
HELEN DREVER

ILLUSTRATED BY
A. MASON TROTTER

THE MORAY PRESS
EDINBURGH & LONDON
1943

EDINBURGH : 21 GEORGE STREET
LONDON : 29 GT. JAMES STREET
BEDFORD ROW, W.C.I

SECOND EDITION REVISED AND CORRECTED

PRINTED IN GREAT BRITAIN BY J. AND J. GRAY, EDINBURGH

FOREWORD

MOST of these Clan Tales were originally written for the B.B.C., and were broadcast during Scottish Children's Hour. Borrowed, as they are, from a variety of sources, it is almost inevitable that there should be slight historical inaccuracies in the tales. But even historians differ in their accounts of happenings among the Scottish clans, so I may claim indulgence for a mere story-teller!

It is impossible to name all the sources of the tales. In addition to books on individual clans, the historians — Browne, Stewart, Gordon and Hume Brown—supplied a good deal of material; so did Eyre-Todd's *Clan History*, Mackay's *Clan Warfare*, and Johnston's *Scottish Clans*. And many of the stories and legends I heard from old folks in the Highlands, who had heard them from their parents and grandparents.

H. D.

TO

J. R. D. AND J. M. D.

CONTENTS

ILLUSTRATIONS

" THE LOCH OF THE SWORDS "

A CLAN DISPUTE

I WONDER whether you have ever heard how the Scottish Clans came into being. It was in this way. The people who lived in the Highlands of Scotland in far-off days had to find some means of protecting themselves and their families from invasion and from being attacked by strong and fierce and often greedy neighbours.

In those days there was no quick way of getting about the country. There were no railways and no motor cars ; even the roads were few and *very* bad !

And although there was always a King of Scotland who made laws, and who appointed officers to carry out these laws and to keep order, there was little or no chance of getting the help of these officials in any dispute because of the great distances and the difficulty of travel. The country was divided into valleys—or straths as they are called—in which the Highlanders lived.

These straths were separated by mountains, rivers and lochs, and by great stretches of moor. Because of this the people were divided into little communities, or Clans, as they were called. A Clan was made up of people, all bearing the same surname and believing themselves to be related to one another and to be descended from the same ancestors. The head of the family was called the Chief of the Clan, and his castle was a kind of palace, to which every man of the Clan was welcome, and to which they all rallied when war broke out.

There were a great many Clans. It was said that at the Battle of Bannockburn at least eighteen Highland chieftains brought their clansmen into the field to support Robert the Bruce. That was in the year 1314. And, just six hundred years later, when the Great War began, the same clan-names were to be found among the soldiers of the Highland regiments ; and among the officers in 1914 there were many direct descendants of the Clan chiefs who fought at Bannockburn !

Each Clan had its own war-cry—or " slogan "— to which every clansman was bound to respond. The slogan was a watch-word in cases of sudden alarm, in the confusion of battle, or in the darkness of night. And every Clan had a place at which they met when the Chief needed help.

In any emergency notice was given to the Clan and those in alliance with them by sending out the Fiery Cross or Tarie. This signal consisted of two pieces of wood in the form of a cross. One of the ends of the horizontal piece was set alight, and from the other end was hung a piece of linen or white cloth stained with blood.

Two fast runners of the Clan, each with a Fiery Cross in his hand, were sent out by the Chief in opposite directions, and, as they ran, they shouted the war-cry of the tribe, and the name of the place where the clansmen were to meet.

When a man became tired he handed over the Cross to another of the Clan, who went on with it. So, as each bearer went at full speed, the Clan was assembled in wonderfully short time.

Land and cattle were the principal possessions of a Clan, and of course well-watered land which was good for grazing cattle was very valuable indeed.

Cattle-stealing (or " lifting," as it was called) was very common, and Clans were continually at war with each other on this account, or about the boundaries of their land.

Sometimes these boundary disputes were settled by agreement between the heads of the Clans, and the following is the story of one of these settlements.

The scene of the story was a small loch called " Loch-na-Clive," which means " The Loch of the Swords," in the centre of which three counties meet —Inverness-shire, Perthshire and Argyllshire.

The story relates that two powerful Clans, Cameron of Lochiel and Murray of Atholl, had, for many years, been at enmity over certain land boundaries. The Chief of the Cameron Clan—and the Earl of

Atholl—Chief of the Murrays—arranged to meet by the side of Loch-na-Clive, in order to settle the dispute. And the chiefs were to come without any followers and just talk the matter over. It was a fine day in late summer. The hills were blue, the water of the rivers and lochs sparkled in the sunshine, and the heather glowed gorgeously purple as Lochiel, accompanied by his favourite collie-dog, walked along to the trysting-place by Loch-na-Clive.

On the way from his own country of Lochaber, Lochiel was met by an old woman of the Clan Cameron, who stopped him on the moor and asked anxiously, " Where are your men, Lochiel ? "

Lochiel just laughed, and said that he needed no men to-day.

But the old woman kept her eyes fixed steadily on his face, and croaked again, " Where are your men, Lochiel ? "

" Peace, old witch ! " said Lochiel, " what need have I to-day of a following ? I go only to meet Atholl, my brother Chief," and strode on.

But the uncanny old woman hobbled after him, caught the flowing end of his cloak and uttered again with strange persistence the question, " Where are your men, Lochiel ? "

The Chief could not help feeling uneasy at this obstinate suggestion of danger and he returned to the nearest clachan (or village) and collected a following of sixty-five men.

They followed him stealthily and when he reached Loch-na-Clive they hid in the deep heather above the loch. Presently the Earl of Atholl was seen striding through the heather, alone, and Lochiel felt ashamed of his hidden company. The two chiefs greeted each other and began to talk of the business about which they had met. But they could not agree, and soon they came to high words. Suddenly Atholl waved his hand in the air and twenty Atholl Highlanders sprang up from the heather behind him.

" Who are these ? " said Lochiel.

" Atholl wethers," said the Earl, with meaning in his tone. " They have come to graze on Lochaber pastures."

Lochiel had arranged with his men that if he needed their help he would turn his cloak so as to show the red lining. So there was a wave of bright red where he stood, and instantly his three-score-and-five warriors came bounding down to the loch side.

Atholl started ; and, " Who are these ? " said he.

" Lochaber dogs," said Lochiel, " sharp-toothed and hungry, and keen to taste the flesh of your Atholl wethers ! Give up, my Lord Earl, your claim to the land, for my dogs are fierce and I cannot much longer hold them in leash ! "

The two chiefs looked at each other, and presently Atholl smiled and held out a hand, which Lochiel grasped.

At that sign of peace, both " dogs " and " wethers " retreated, and sank down again among the heather ; and the chiefs, now in friendly spirit, discussed the business of the boundary.

A settlement was at length reached, and the Earl of Atholl, drawing his sword from its sheath and kissing it, renounced his claim to the land in dispute " through summer's heat and winter's cold." Then he whirled it round his head and with a great sweep it disappeared in the waters of Loch-na-Clive. And Atholl proclaimed that until the sword was found again, the land should be Lochiel's land.

Three centuries have passed since then ; but one day about a hundred years ago a boy fishing in the loch drew up a rusty broadsword with a basket hilt, and, very much pleased with his strange " fish," carried it up to show to the minister of the parish. But the Lochaber men were much alarmed at hearing of the boy's unusual " catch " and they would not sleep a night until it was restored to the watery bed where it had slept for two hundred years !

I

SOMERLED OF THE ISLES

ANCESTOR OF CLAN DONALD

SUCH reliable information as we possess about the forebears of Clan Donald starts with Gille Adamnan, the grandfather of Somerled of the Isles. For many years before Somerled's time the north and west of Scotland was being harassed by the raids of powerful enemies from outside the kingdom. These were the Northmen—or vikings—who came from Norway, Sweden and Denmark. They were splendid fighters and born sailors, their ships being the largest and fastest on the seas. These ships were shaped like dragons, the bow being built to look like a dragon's head, while the stern formed its tail. There were places for as many as sixty rowers in most of the viking ships. At first these Norsemen landed only to plunder and destroy, and dash off again. But a time came when they were not content to stop at that—when their idea was to conquer land in which to settle.

The islands were fairly easy prey for them, and in course of time they took possession of Orkney, Shetland, and the Western Isles ; and parts of Caithness and Sutherland as well. Then they turned their attention to the mainland of Argyll. Somerled's grandfather owned a large part of Argyll, but he was not powerful enough to keep the vikings at bay, and after one ineffectual attempt he was driven out of the country. With his son, Gillebrighde or Gilbert, he took refuge in the north of Ireland, where he died. By and by Gilbert began to long to see his native land again, and he and his son, named Somerled, managed to return to Argyll. But they found themselves homeless wanderers there, and they settled in a cave on the shores of Loch Linnhe, where they lived in direst poverty.

Gilbert's fighting days were over, and Somerled spent his time in brooding over the ruined fortunes of his house. But something happened to change all this, and, from being a depressed dreamer, Somerled suddenly developed into a master of warlike strategy.

The Clan MacInnes (who are a sept or ally of the Clan Macdonald) had come to Morven in Argyll on a foraging expedition. The Norsemen appeared unexpectedly, and in a skirmish with them the MacInnes leader was killed. So the Clan found themselves leaderless, and practically in sight of the enemy as well, for the viking galleys lay just off the shore. No man among the clansmen was qualified to lead them into battle, and they knew of no one on the spot who could step into the breach. So they formed a council which agreed on rather a reckless plan. This was to go along by the shore hills and invite the first person whom they should see to become their leader against the vikings! They set off and, when they had reached the rocky banks of a fishing stream called the " Gearr Abhainn " (" Garven "), whom should they see but Somerled with his rod, angling for his next meal!

In spite of their desperate situation they could not help raising a great shout of laughter! Somerled asked the reason for their mirth. It was rather an awkward question to answer, but they said it was just a shout of joy at seeing him! The fact was that they looked upon poor Somerled as a sort of half-wit because of his melancholy manner. But they had sworn to take as leader the first man they should see, and in fulfilment of that vow they now asked Somerled to be their leader. He thought about it for some time without answering, and suddenly

B

there came a tug at his line ! " See now," he said,
" I have hooked a salmon. Let it give you my
answer. If I can land the fish, my help shall be
yours ! " As it happened, it was a very sportive
fish and difficult to catch, and the MacInnes men
saw a thrilling fight between man and salmon as it
plunged and struggled up and down the river. But
Somerled was a good fisher, and at last the salmon
lay quivering on the bank. Then Somerled turned
and said, " My help is yours ! But—to begin with—
having of your own accord invited me to lead you,
you must swear to obey my commands." Quite
delighted at this exhibition of authority from the
supposed dreamer, they acknowledged their new
general and gave him on the spot their oath of
allegiance.

He appointed a place where they were to muster,
and giving orders to light a great number of fires
round their encampment, he said that he would join
them later. He carried the salmon to the cave, where
he cooked it and left it ready for his father's meal ;
and then went to take up his command.

At early morning he saw the viking ships landing
their forces. These completely outnumbered his
men ; so he made a plan by which to deceive the
enemy as to his own numbers. A herd of cattle lay
in a neighbouring valley and he at once ordered
them to be killed and skinned. He occupied a
position which commanded a full view of the enemy's

movements ; and as soon as he saw them forming their ranks he ordered his small force to march down the valley and go round a hill at the foot— coming back to the place where they started from. They kept on marching round and round the hill, and the enemy thought that they were a formidable battalion. Next, ordering every man to wrap himself in an ox hide with the smooth side out, they did the same thing all over again several times, which gave the appearance of another (and different) battalion. After that Somerled ordered his men to turn the *rough* side of the hides outward, and the wild and savage appearance of this supposed *third* battalion was too much for the Norsemen, who, falling into disorder, gave way to panic and fled in all directions. Seeing this, Somerled and his fierce-looking little force, wildly yelling, charged down the slope, and cut down the viking advance party with great slaughter. The rest made for the ships and got away as fast as possible.

Somerled followed up this victory with others, and eventually driving the Norsemen out of the Western Highlands, he made himself master of Lochaber, Morven, and northern Argyll. Meanwhile, David II was driving them from the Isle of Man, Arran and Bute, and Somerled for his assistance and daring got a grant of these islands from the King.

In the Western Isles, however, the viking power

was still unbroken, and he was determined to be ruler of these also. The King of the Isles at that time was a viking called Olaf the Red, who had a daughter, Ragnhildis. Somerled made up his mind that, although he could not take the islands by force, there was a way of getting a footing there. This was to marry Ragnhildis. Whether Ragnhildis wanted to marry Somerled did not enter into the question, but he carried her off.

Perhaps she did not mind being carried off by such a famous warrior ; she certainly married him ! They had three sons, Dugall, Reginald and Angus. Dugall founded the Clan MacDougal, and inherited Lorn, Jura and Mull when his father died. Reginald got Kintyre and Islay ; and Bute and Arran fell to Angus.

Reginald, through his son Donald, founded the famous Clan MacDonald. He took the title of " King," and later " Lord of the Isles," which latter became a hereditary title in the family.

Clan MacDonald, which was very powerful and included many branches, always took a prominent share in the turmoils which kept the Highlands in active ferment during several hundred years. They were entirely loyal to the Stewarts, and took an active share in helping and sheltering Prince Charlie in his wanderings after Culloden.

II

CLAN CAMPBELL

"THE LEGEND OF KILCHURN"

THE pedigree of the Campbells can be traced back to the thirteenth century when the family was first mentioned in important Scottish documents. They got that name, it is said, because of an ancestor who had a facial peculiarity of some sort, for in the Gaelic the words " cam beul " mean " wry mouth."

Highland names were often the result of some personal defect or attribute, " Malcolm Canmore," for instance. " Can mohr " means the " big head," and so we got " Malcolm with the Big Head."

Campbell is the surname of the Dukes of Argyll. The first Duke was called " Cailean Mor," which means " Big Colin " ; and ever since his day the Clan title for the Chief has been " Mic Cailean Mor," or " Son of Big Colin." The Dukes of Argyll are looked up to with the most profound reverence by their kinsmen and clansmen, and are regarded by them as more important than Royalty itself ! When Queen Victoria's daughter, the Princess Louise, married the Marquis of Lorne (who was the eldest son of the Duke of Argyll) the Campbell Clan did not consider that a special honour had been paid to the Scottish family ! Not a bit of it ! What they said on the day of the wedding was, " Isn't it proud that the Queen will be this day, that her daughter has got the son of Mic Cailean Mor for her husband ! "

Next in rank to the Dukes of Argyll are their cousins, the Campbells of Breadalbane. The ancestor of this branch was Sir Colin Campbell— " Cailean Dubh na Roimhe " (Black Colin of Rome). He received, as his inheritance from his father, the lands of Glenorchy, after the MacGregors had been driven from them. And here is a story of that Sir Colin, Knight-Templar and Lord of Kilchurn Castle—the ruins of which can still be seen on a peninsula on Loch Awe in Argyllshire.

Judging from what remains of the castle and from the commanding position which it occupies, it is easy to see that it must have been in its day a very important stronghold. There was a great tower, five stories high, which is said to have been planned and added to by Lady Campbell, when her husband was away fighting in the Crusades. The Knights Templars were the most important and most powerful of the great military orders of the Middle Ages. The object of the order was a noble one. It was to maintain, by force of arms if necessary, a free passage for pilgrims who wanted to visit the Holy Sepulchre in Jerusalem. Fighting in the Crusades meant long absence from home, so, when Sir Colin went away to Europe and Palestine, his lady knew that there would be a period of loneliness before her, with but scanty news of her husband's doings.

Accompanying Sir Colin on the expedition were men of his own Clan, one of whom was sent back to Scotland at regular intervals to tell Lady Campbell and their young son how Sir Colin was getting on. During his absence which had extended for over seven years, he was for a time in Rome, where he had a very singular and disturbing dream about his wife and his home. He tried to forget the dream, but it preyed on his mind to such an extent that he confided it and his fears to one of the monks. In those days people believed greatly in dreams and what they foretold, and the monk at once advised Sir Colin to go home, because, in his opinion, a very serious domestic calamity threatened. Acting on his advice Sir Colin left for Scotland. After encountering many dangers and difficulties he reached a place near Glasgow called Succoth, which is still owned by a branch of the Campbell family. At Succoth there lived an old woman of his Clan. This old woman in his early days had been his nurse. In the disguise of a beggar he arrived at her cottage at nightfall and knocked at the door. When she opened the door she saw what she supposed to be a poor beggar man, who asked her for food and shelter. She at once asked him to come in and sit by the fire, and she set about making some porridge for her visitor. As he stretched out his hands to the blaze of the fire, her startled eyes lighted on a peculiarly shaped scar on his arm. " Oh, Cailean Dubh, Cailean Dubh ! my bairn that I nursed ! " she cried. " It is myself that knows that scar ! " And she wept in her joy, for she had supposed him to be dead. She hastened to tell him all that had happened in his absence, and the story supplied a reason for the uneasiness caused by his dream. It appeared that for some years no word of any kind had been received in Argyllshire with regard to Sir Colin, nor had any of the letters been delivered which he had sent to his wife. Not only that, but news had been circulated that he had been killed in battle in the Holy Land.

Now Sir Colin knew that someone must have played him false ; he had repeatedly sent home clansmen with letters and news for his wife, and it

SHE HASTENED TO TELL HIM ALL THAT HAD HAPPENED IN HIS ABSENCE

was scarcely possible that *every* messenger sent by
him should have perished before reaching Scotland.
His old nurse was able to supply the explanation and
justify his suspicions.

All the rumours about his death had come
apparently from one source. This was a neighbouring laird, the Baron McCorquodale, who—as was
eventually proved—had intercepted and killed or
else imprisoned every one of Sir Colin's messengers.
By degrees he induced Lady Campbell to believe in
her husband's death, and at last he proposed marriage to her; and she (believing that he was her best
friend) accepted him.

This was the news that his old nurse had for Sir
Colin; and further, the marriage was fixed for the
following day! Indignant at what he had heard,
Sir Colin set out for Kilchurn early next morning.
As he followed the romantic windings of the River
Orchy, the lively sounds of the bagpipe and the gay
shouts of his clansmen assembled to join in the
festivity were borne to his ears on the breeze. He
crossed the drawbridge and entered the gates of
the castle, which on this important occasion were
open to all. Nobody recognised him, for he still
wore his beggar's rags. He stood for a little, silently
gazing on the scene of excitement and feasting,
until one of the servants asked him what he wanted.
"To have my hunger satisfied and my thirst
quenched," he said; and at once food and drink

were brought to him. He ate, but he refused to drink, making the request that the lady of the castle would give him a cup with her own hands and allow him to drink to her health. Lady Campbell was told of this strange request from a beggar ; and being always charitable and benevolent she came at once and handed him a cup of wine. Sir Colin drank to her health, and as he handed back the empty cup he dropped a ring into it. The lady observing his action took out the ring and examined it. To her amazement she found it to be a ring which she had given to her husband when he departed for the Holy Land, and which he had promised to keep as a talisman on the field of battle and his most sacred possession. Greatly agitated she said to the beggar, " Speak, man ! Where got ye this ring ? Got ye it on sea or got ye it on land, or got ye it on a dead man's hand ? " And Sir Colin, gazing earnestly at her, said, " I neither got it on sea, nor got I it on land, nor yet on a dead man's hand. I got it from you on our parting day and I give it to you on your wedding day ! " With that he let his beggar's cloak fall from him and he stood revealed to the astonished company in the white cloak of the Knight-Templar with the scarlet cross on the breast—their own lost Sir Colin !

" Oh ! my husband, my husband ! " cried Lady Campbell, full of joy, as she threw herself into his arms. A shout of delight from his clansmen rent the air, and the pipers made the castle resound with the pibroch of the Campbells. Baron McCorquodale was allowed to depart unnoticed. In their joy at being reunited, Sir Colin and his lady were generous to the traitor and let him go unpunished.

But after the death of Sir Colin some years later, his son, " Black Colin " the second, avenged the wrong done to his father, and took from the Baron his lands and possessions.

III

CLAN MACKENZIE

" THE CABERFEIDH "

HUNDREDS of years ago, a song made in praise of the Chief of the Clan Mackenzie began like this :

" Kenneth MacKenneth, great Earl of the North,
 The Lord of Loch Carron, Glenshiel and Seaforth."

Now, looking at a map of Ross-shire you see that Glencarron and Glenshiel are on the west of the county, while on the east, not very far from Dingwall, is Brahan Castle and Seaforth's largest estate. So that the old saying, that " the lands of the Mackenzies stretched from sea to sea " was quite true. Two earldoms (those of Seaforth and Cromartie) belong to the Clan, as well as four baronetcies. The Mackenzies have always been a loyal Clan. One chief went with James I on an expedition to the north ; another fought with James IV at Flodden, and was nearly captured by the English. A third fought for Mary Queen of Scots at the Battle of Langside.

The Clan took part in several Jacobite risings and had their estates forfeited to the Crown. They were also deprived of the Earldom of Seaforth. But the Kenneth who was the Chief in 1770 bought back his property from the Crown and was again made Earl of Seaforth. To show his gratitude he and the Clan the following year raised the regiment of the Seaforth Highlanders.

The crest used by the Chief of the Clan is a stag's head and the granting of this crest makes an interesting story.

Back in the thirteenth century, Alexander III, King of Scotland, was hunting in the Forest of Mar in the Grampian Mountains. A royal stag hunt— to which the chiefs of all the great Highland Clans had been invited—was in progress. Among the chiefs was Kenneth of Kintail, Chief of the Mackenzies. It was a fine day for sport. The hounds were keen on the scent, and stag after stag fell to the arrows of the party—for in those days firearms were not used for sport. The King, who was a very enthusiastic sportsman, spied away up the valley the great antlers of a fine stag, and the hounds were sent to drive it down. This they did, and down the gully towards the King and his companions came the handsome hunted beast. To the dismay of Alexander and the horror of his company, the infuriated animal lowered its antlers and charged straight at the King, who was entirely at its mercy. Before any of the other chieftains could stir, Kenneth of Kintail dashed to the King's rescue, shouting the Gaelic words, " Cuidich an Righ ! Cuidich an Righ ! " (" Save the King ! Save the King ! ") He drew his bow ; an arrow sped through the air. It was a risky shot, for it might easily have hit the King instead of the stag. But Kenneth aimed true. The arrow pierced the stag—and the King was saved ! The King in token of his gratitude granted to the Mackenzie Chief a stag's head, to be the armorial bearings of the family for all time, with the motto " Cuidich an Righ," and confirmed him in possession of the lands of Kintail.

Five hundred years later, when the regiment of the Seaforth Highlanders was raised, they were allowed to use both crest and motto. It is the only Highland regiment in the Army which uses a Clan crest and motto.

The Macdonalds of the Isles (Somerled's descendants) were at one time the most powerful Clan in the Highlands. When they went to war they could demand, as a right, the military help of the Mackenzies and the Rosses. But when these Clans themselves grew powerful, they broke away from the Lord of the Isles and refused to take part in his quarrels. Feeling ran high then, especially between the Mackenzies and the Macdonalds, until the fifteenth century, when Kenneth, the son of the Chief of Kintail, married a daughter of the Lord of the Isles. But no peace could last between these Clans and very soon there was a new quarrel. One of those Macdonalds who had come into possession of Balconie Castle, on the Cromarty Firth, gave a great entertainment to the gentry of Ross-shire, who poured in from all over the county. Night quarters were allotted to the guests as they arrived, for hospitality in the Highlands was no one-night affair ; it was on a most lavish scale and lasted for several days. Almost the last to come, as it happened (and rather an unexpected guest) was Kenneth of Kintail, with a band of his clansmen. Macdonald had by this time allotted all the sleeping-rooms in the castle—what on earth was to be done with the Mackenzies ? The only place available was a large kiln and this he offered to Kenneth and his party, with the hint that as he was now a relative by marriage, he would not expect to stand on ceremony. But the offer was taken as a deliberate insult ; Kenneth flew into a great rage and out came the

c

Mackenzies' weapons ! But Kenneth restrained them and retired with them to the Black Isle, to settle how to avenge the affront. The news went round the rest of the Clan, which rose in its wrath and made ready for battle. But first of all Kenneth was determined in his rage to be done with the Macdonalds for good—and he sent his wife back to her family. It is said that she was blind in one eye and that he added insult to injury by sending, as her escort, a one-eyed servant, a one-eyed horse, and a one-eyed dog ! Naturally that added fuel to the Macdonald fire. The Battle of the Park—as it was called—between the two Clans took place at Jamestown, between Strathpeffer and the River Conon. The men of Strathconon (who were mostly Mac-Lennans and MacRaes, septs of the Caberfeidh) were the most famous archers in the Highlands, so you may be sure they were called on to rally to Kenneth's standard. In the battle Kenneth scored a great victory and, in defeating the Macdonalds, he struck a blow which had lasting effects on Highland history. His name has been handed down to his descendants as " Kenneth of the Battle."

At that time the River Conon, being in flood, was very wide, and the routed Macdonalds could not find the fords by which to cross. It is said that, after the battle, an old Jamestown woman who was cutting fodder for her cow was asked by some retreating Macdonalds " where the ford was ? " She said, " Iss it the ford you are wanting ? Well, indeed, and iss not the whole river just a big ford ! " Believing her, they dashed into the river, which at once swept them off their feet. One or two of them grasped tree-branches overhanging the banks, whereupon this bloodthirsty old dame promptly used a sickle and cut the branches to which the men clung ! As they were swept away she said, " Thieves that you are, be going ! The Mackenzies will not grudge you a few of their branches ! "

After the Battle of Culloden, the quick wit and devotion of a member of the Mackenzie Clan greatly helped Prince Charlie when he was hard pressed. This was Roderick Mackenzie, who had served as one of the Prince's life-guards. About the same age and build, his features were sufficiently like those of Charles to deceive a casual observer. Near the Prince's hiding-place in Glenmoriston he was surprised and overcome by some of Cumberland's soldiers, who were all eager to win the £30,000 which had been set on the Prince's head. Nothing could save Roderick, but he saw a way to shield Charles, and he called out loudly as he fell, " Villains ! you have killed your Prince ! You have killed your Prince ! " The soldiers who had not been quite certain of the identity of their victim were overjoyed at their supposed good fortune, and hurried to claim the £30,000. The Duke of Cumberland, equally delighted, immediately set out for London to have the head identified as that of Prince Charles. The mistake was of course discovered, but the delay enabled the Prince to escape from Glenmoriston and take refuge with Cluny Macpherson at " The Cage." And now, away above Glenmoriston can be seen a great heap of stones which is called " Mackenzie's Cairn." It is a lasting memorial to the resource and sacrifice of Roderick of the Caberfeidh.

Shortly after the Seaforth Highlanders had been raised in Ross-shire, the regiment marched to Leith to embark for foreign service. While at Leith some cause of discontent occurred among them and they refused to embark. Instead, they marched out of the town with pipes playing and two Mackenzie tartan plaids for regimental colours fixed on poles. They marched up Arthur's Seat and stayed there for several days, getting supplies from people who sympathised with them. The Earls of Seaforth and Dunmore and other Highland gentlemen made inquiries into the causes of their complaints and, finding these justified, had them removed; so the soldiers, being now satisfied, marched down the hill with pipes playing and the two earls and General Skene at their head. The Highlanders went back to Leith, pleased that they had proved their Highland independence. It was said that the MacRaes, who were strongly represented in the regiment, were the ringleaders in this disturbance, which has always been known as " The Affair of the MacRaes."

IV

CLAN MACKAY OF STRATHNAVER

" SIOL MHORGAN "

FEW of the Highland Clans are so uncertain
of their origin as the Mackays of Strathnaver—
or Clan Morgan as they were first called.
The popular opinion is that they were derived from
the same root as the Forbeses, who are an Aberdeenshire Clan. This opinion is supported by an
eleventh-century manuscript which shows that the
lands of the Abbey of Deer, in Aberdeenshire, were
granted to Clan Morgan. The Mackays themselves
must have believed in the Forbes connection because, in 1608, they adopted the Forbes badge and

armorial bearings (with slight differences) by per-
mission of Lord Forbes, whom Mackay of Farr
called his " Dear Chief."

Norwegian sagas tell us that the ancestor of the
race was a " Jarl "—which probably means the same
thing as a " Mormaer," the old Celtic title of the
ruler of a province.

It is practically certain that the original Clan
Mackay or Morgan was one of the warlike tribes that
Malcolm IV could not control in Moray, as Aberdeenshire was then called, when Angus, and later his
son MacEth, were rulers of the province.   At last
Malcolm split up the tribes, expelling them by force
to various parts of the country.

The Clan Morgan went northwards, where Mac-
Eth's daughter was married to the Norse Earl of
Caithness ; and he gave the incomers the Strath of
Naver in which to settle.   There they were sur-
rounded by powerful Clans.

South of them were the Macleods and the Earl
of Sutherland ; east of them the Gunns and the
Sinclairs.

They had no charter of land from the King ; they
held their land entirely by the sword until the year
1499.

For about a hundred and fifty years they warred,
now with one neighbour, now with another ; occasionally combining with one of the very tribes against
whom their attacks had previously been directed.

According to the historian, Sir Robert Gordon, the Chief of their tribe left two sons, called Morgan and Farquhar. Through Morgan came the Clan name " Siol Mhorgan " (the race of Morgan). A son married a MacNeil of Gigha and the son of this marriage was a born leader. He was named " Aodh " (Iye), and from him the Clan took its name Mac-Aodh or Mackay.

Angus Dubh (Black Angus) was another famous Mackay warrior. He was known as " Angus the Absolute " and it was said that he could summon four thousand men to the field.

When James I came to Scotland, one of his first acts was, under pretence of friendship, to invite forty of the great Highland chiefs to meet him in Inverness. But when the chiefs appeared they were all made prisoners by the King. Angus was among them and before he could be set free he had to give his son Neil as a hostage. Poor Neil was kept prisoner on the Bass Rock for ten years, and meanwhile Angus sent for " Iain Aberach," his youngest son, who had been brought up in Lochaber among his mother's people. Iain obeyed his father's summons at once, walking all the long way from Lochaber to Strathnaver, through the wild mountains of Inverness-shire, by the wide firths and fertile lands of Easter Ross, and on through the broad moors and great bens of Sutherland. He carried no baggage. His plaid served him as cloak by day and blanket by night. When he arrived he was tired and hungry, and he asked for food. Angus told him that he would find all he wanted " and perhaps more " in the dining-chamber—so off Iain went. He opened the door and saw food in abundance on the table, but the food was guarded by a great fierce boar-hound ! That was Angus's way of testing the courage of his young (and almost unknown) son ! The animal bounded towards the stranger and leapt at his throat—truly a strange welcome for a hungry lad ! But Iain was brave though hungry and he had just time to snatch out his dirk when the hound was upon him. He struck with sure aim—and yet unwillingly, for he hated killing such a beautiful dog. But Angus was glad to see that the men of Lochaber had taught his boy to carry a stout heart, and in his joy he exclaimed, " Dearbh thu do chridhe ! " (" You have proved your valour ! ") And ever since, the Aberach family have used these words as their motto or war-cry, " Bi treun ! " (" Be valiant ! ") being the slogan of all the other Mackays.

Before he died, Angus the Absolute was to see this young son of his " prove his valour " in a great battle in which he led the Mackays to victory. This was at Drumnacoub near Tongue, against the Earl of Sutherland. By that time Angus was past wielding a sword in battle ; but he met his death on the field all the same. After the fight was over he went to see what he could do for his wounded clansmen, and he was killed by an arrow from a skulking assassin of a Sutherland man ! Naturally that made the feud more bitter than ever and clan fights succeeded each other year in and year out.

There was one occasion when the Mackays got into dreadful disgrace. A party led by Neil's son chased some enemies into the Chapel of St. Duthus at Tain, in Ross-shire, and killed them. Not content with that they set fire to the chapel ! The Tain people were of course furious, for the church was considered to be sanctuary for refugees. Besides which, was it not in that very chapel that Malcolm Canmore had granted a Royal Charter to the Burgh of Tain ! It was a terrible deed and the Mackay leader was captured and executed.

In the time of Charles I, Donald, Chief of the Clan, was raised to the peerage and became Lord Reay. One result of these centuries of clan feuds had been to make a splendid fighting race of the Mackays. Lord Reay saw this and he organised their fighting powers by raising a brigade of over two thousand men for military service with the King of Denmark. After this service, they enlisted under Prince Gustavus Adolphus of Sweden, and fought for the Protestant cause in Europe in the Thirty Years' War. During that war the Mackays distinguished themselves over and over again, and earned the greatest praise for their endurance and valour. They in turn regarded the Prince with great respect and affection. They paid him what is considered a high honour in the Highlands, when his name was given to many a Mackay baby born about that time, and since handed down in their families. So if we meet someone called Gustavus Mackay, we may safely conclude that one of his ancestors fought under the Swedish Prince three hundred years ago.

An officer of the Mackay Brigade, General Hugh Mackay of Scourie, was so distinguished as to be invited by two kings at the same time to come and command their rival armies ! These kings were William of Orange and James II of England. The general accepted William's offer and went to Holland ; and so began the Dutch connection of the Mackays. One branch of the family settled there and was granted a title and an estate by the Government of Holland.

Another member of the Clan was a distinguished poet called Rob Donn Mackay, whose poems are among the best in Gaelic literature. He began life as a herdsman and afterwards became the steward of Lord Reay. When he was forty-five years of age a French invasion threatened our shores and the Earl of Sutherland raised a battalion of Sutherland Highlanders to help defend them. Some people say that poets are dreamers, but Rob Donn was no dreamer, for he at once offered himself and served in the regiment for eight years. Not a bit like a

certain bard belonging to another Clan, who began
fighting in a battle, but, when things got very hot,
he ran away and hid himself. He explained afterwards that, of course, he wasn't a bit *afraid*—or
anything of that sort—but that it would be such a
pity if no one could write a poem about the battle,
and he was just making sure !

After that war Lord Reay sold Strathnaver to the
Earl of Sutherland, so that there is very little Mackay
land now in the North of Scotland.

It is a long, long time since these feuds, and the
Mackays live now at peace with their neighbours.
But for years jealousy smouldered amongst the
dependants of the rival chiefs, and offence was
always quick to be taken. There is a story that once
the Earl of Sutherland sent one of his retainers with
a message from Dunrobin Castle to the House of
Tongue, Lord Reay's family seat. It is a long distance away and the Dunrobin man had to stay at
Tongue overnight. At bedtime he took off his
shoes (or " cuarans," as they were called) of un-
dressed leather, and put them on the dresser in the
kitchen ; which annoyed the cook exceedingly, for
she took it as a deliberate insult. Next morning,
for breakfast, she gave the Dunrobin man a very
large substantial-looking pie. He ate every bit of
it, and then he said he must be " taking the road,"
and would she get his cuarans for him ? She gave
a peculiar smile and said to him, " Well now, I

hope that you enjoyed your breakfast ? " " Yess,
inteet," he answered. " It was the fine breakfast
whatefer. Inteet, I'm thinking I'll not be needing
any dinner after it, at all, at all ! But now I am
looking for my cuarans, for I must be going."
" Well indeed," said the cook, " it's not looking
for your cuarans you need to be, for they are inside
you—and a fine breakfast they made whatefer !
And that will be teaching you to put your upstart
Sutherland cuarans on a shentleman's dresser ! "

V

CLAN CAMERON

" THE CAMERON MEN "

THE name " Cameron " is made up of two Gaelic words—" cam," meaning wry or crooked, and " sron " meaning nose. So an ancestor of the Clan must have had a crooked nose ! The first Cameron chief who was famous in history was Donald Dhu (Black Donald), and each chief since his time has been called Mic Donuil Dhu (Son of Black Donald). The Camerons have a belief that they are descended from one of the Danish royal family, who, fifteen hundred years ago, helped a Scottish king to win back his throne.

But whatever their origin, whether royal or merely noble, it is certain that no name is more popular in the Highlands than that of Cameron. And the name of Lochiel, the Chief of the Clan, has always stood for everything that is honourable and good.

Lochaber in Inverness-shire is the home country of the clan. It is a wild and beautiful region, broken up by great bens and glens, with lovely lochs and rushing mountain rivers to keep it green and fertile.

The way in which places and family names are allied is characteristic all through the Highlands. Who, for example, can separate the name of Glencoe from thoughts of the Macdonalds ; Appin from the Stewarts ; Balquhidder from the Maclarens and Macgregors ?—and so on.

So it is in Lochaber. The mere mention of Loch Eil, Loch Arkaig, Loch Lochy—and the Camerons are with us !—Sir Ewan, who was such a thorn in the side of Cromwell's soldiers ; the Gentle Lochiel of Prince Charlie's day ; Dr. Archie Cameron, physician, and martyr to the Stewart cause ; Cameron of Fassifern, the hero of Quatre Bras ; and always inseparable from these—the Cameron Men !

There are several historic lochs in Lochaber. There is lonely Loch Treig, surrounded by pre-cipitous hills rising sheer from the water, and at one end an islet called the Council Island.

Many a time have the Camerons convoyed their Chief to the loch when he went on the island to confer with the Mackintosh over some Clan dispute. It was selected as the meeting-place because there the two chiefs could be alone with no risk of being ambushed. On the hillside and overhanging the loch is a huge boulder called the Watch Rock, from which Cameron sentinels could keep an eye on the welfare of their Chief!

More lonely still is the little Loch of the Swords where an old-standing boundary dispute was settled between Lochiel and Murray of Atholl. The whole beautiful region abounds in Clan memories. Little wonder if Camerons in foreign countries should be homesick for the sight of it! It is said that during the wars abroad the pipers had actually to be forbidden to play the old tune, *Farewell to Lochaber*, because of its depressing effect on the spirits of the Cameron Highlanders. But homesickness soon disappeared when it came to fighting, for then the enemy found himself faced by men who did not know the meaning of the word " defeat."

Most people know Fort William as it is to-day. It was built in Cromwell's time, and used as a fort. It was, in fact, the headquarters of the English troops that were sent to keep the Camerons in order. Long after the other Clans had given in, they stood out, and many a fierce skirmish they had with the Sassenachs. There was one occasion when Lochiel and his clansmen were in a very tight corner indeed! They had been defending one end of a mountain pass, when they found themselves being attacked from the other end as well ! Capture seemed to stare them in the face—but they were not done yet ! Slowly and in regular formation they retreated—up the steep mountain-side. Facing their enemies they stepped—back and up, back and up, in perfect order ! The hillsides were deep with snow, and the Englishmen, unused to such ground, did not dare to follow. They could only watch, and gasp with amazement and unwilling admiration, when at last the gallant band, still facing them, disappeared from view over the high hilltop !

The Highland soldiers were inured to all sorts of hardships. It is told that the fighting father of Cameron sons considered himself disgraced one night during this campaign, when sleeping out in the snow with his company.

This Cameron saw one of his sons make a large snowball for a pillow, and, full of contempt, he got up and kicked it away, saying, " Are you become so like a woman that you cannot sleep without such luxury ? "

Following the lead of their Chief the Camerons were always devoted adherents of the Stewarts. They fought at Killiecrankie, where Lochiel's counsel to " fight immediately while the men were in good heart " prevailed, and justified itself.

At the Jacobite Rebellion of 1715 Sir Ewan Cameron was an old man, but his son, Allan, attended the Chevalier when he came from France to take part in the campaign. A curious incident happened at this time. Very early on the morning on which the Chevalier de St. George (son of James II) landed at Peterhead, Sir Ewan started from his sleep and called out to Lady Cameron, " Wife, wife ! The King has landed ! The King has landed,—and our son Allan is with him ! "

Lady Cameron told him he had been dreaming, but he repeated his words, and, rising in haste, he roused the household and commanded a large bon-fire to be built.

Then the best liquor in the house had to be brought out so that all his " lads "—as he called his clansmen—and friends might be able to drink the King's health. His lady said that he was very foolish to make all these preparations because of a dream, but he was so urgent and gave such definite com-mands that, against her own judgment, she was inspired to fall in with his mood, and help with a will in the great doings. All the people in the neighbourhood were commanded to the festivity, which went on—Highland fashion—for two days. News took long to travel then, but, before many days, definite tidings reached Lochaber to confirm the fact that the day and the hour of the arrival of the Prince and his attendants (among whom was Allan Cameron) exactly coincided with Sir Ewan's announcement to his wife !

D

When Prince Charlie landed in Scotland, Sir Ewan's grandson, Donald—called the " Gentle Lochiel "—was one of the first nobles summoned to meet him. Lochiel knew quite well that the Jacobite cause was a forlorn hope, for Charles had neither money nor resources ; and he begged the Prince to wait until he had some more definite support. But the Prince was impatient with this wise counsel and he exclaimed angrily, " In a few days, with the few friends that I have, I will erect the Royal Standard and proclaim to the people of Britain that Charles Stuart has come over to claim the crown of his ancestors. And Lochiel may stay at home, and from the newspapers learn the fate of his Prince ! " But Lochiel exclaimed, " No ! I'll share the fate of my Prince, and so shall every man over whom Nature or Fortune has given me any power ! " When Charles with only a hundred and fifty followers went to erect his standard at Loch Shiel in Glen Finnan, he found the place quiet and deserted, and his spirits were low indeed. But by and by there came the distant sound of pipes, and soon the notes of a Cameron pibroch, accompanied by the regular tramp of feet, were borne on the wind towards him. Then over the crest of a hill appeared a line of tartan. The line became a glowing mass which spread down over the hillside, drawing nearer in regular formation. It was the Cameron Men, nearly eight hundred strong ! Then, and only then, the Prince gave his banner to the Marquis of Tullibardine to unfurl—and so began the great " Rising of the 'Forty-five ! "

Lochiel fulfilled his promise to Prince Charlie nobly and unsparingly. In his service he gave all—home, health and liberty. He was wounded in both ankles at Culloden. Along with the Prince he hid in his own woods of Achnacarry, in a cave in the neighbourhood, in Cluny Macpherson's Cage on Ben Alder. Later he accompanied Prince Charlie to France, but he died there in the year 1748.

Dr. Archibald Cameron, brother of the Gentle Lochiel, was another to suffer in the Stewart cause. He escaped to France, but returning to Scotland on various missions he was caught at last. He was the last Jacobite to pay the extreme penalty.

In later days one of the most distinguished members of the Clan was Captain John Cameron of Fassifern. An able and brilliant soldier, his military career was cut short during the Napoleonic Wars at Quatre Bras in 1815, when, at the command of the Duke of Wellington, he led his regiment, the famous 92nd, in a glorious charge, in which, alas ! he was mortally wounded. " How goes the day ? " he asked anxiously, and when told, " All's well," he said, " I die happy, and I trust my dear country will believe I have served her faithfully."

The charge of the 92nd at Quatre Bras has been the subject of many patriotic poems, one of the

best known being that of Professor Blackie, which
finishes with the verse :

" And now he sleeps—for they bore him home
   When the war was done, across the foam—
   Beneath the shadow of Nevis Ben
   With his sires, the pride of the Cameron men.
   Three thousand Highlandmen stood around
   As they laid him to rest on his native ground ;
   The Cameron brave, whose eye never quailed,
   Whose heart never sank and whose hand never
       failed,
   When the Cameron men were wanted ! "

VI

CLAN MACGREGOR

" NAMELESS BY DAY ! "

THE ill-fated Clan Alpin or MacGregor claims descent from an early Scottish King, called Kenneth Alpin. So the MacGregors adopted as their motto the Gaelic words " S'rioghal mo dhream " (" Royal is my race "). Because of an adventure of one of their early chiefs the motto was changed later to " E'en do and spare not ! "

In days when wild boars were common in Scotland a MacGregor went out to attend his King on a hunting expedition. An enormous wild boar was encountered and the King pursued it. But it happened that he was no match for that particular boar and instead of attacking he found himself attacked ! MacGregor had no wish to spoil sport, but he saw that the King was in danger and he called out to ask whether he should help him, getting the prompt answer, " E'en do and spare not ! " And the story goes that MacGregor tore up a young oak-tree by the roots and used it in his left hand to keep off the infuriated animal until he got a chance to kill it with his sword ; and after that incident the King's words were used as the MacGregor motto. The shield in the MacGregor coat-of-arms shows the oak-tree, with a sword across it, which bears on its point a crown—to show that it was used in a king's service.

In the eleventh century the MacGregors were a flourishing Clan and a knighthood was given to their Chief, while his son was made Abbot of Dunkeld. Then they became Lords of Glenorchy, and were an important Highland family. While Robert the Bruce was struggling for the independence of Scotland, the MacGregors were his loyal supporters. They sheltered Bruce in a cave on Loch Lomond side until they could get him taken across the Loch and conveyed from there to his own part of the country. The east side of Loch Lomond was one of the boundaries of the wide MacGregor country. It was well guarded by great mountains and deep forests ; so the Clan was able to settle in kindly valleys, safe from marauders, and out of reach of the laws and forces of the Scots Government.

Their fortunes took an evil turn, and the cause was surely the strangest that ever brought about the downfall of a great family. It was—a black sheep with a white tail! In the sixteenth century two MacGregors found themselves in the Colquhoun country, which lies at Luss, on the west bank of Loch Lomond. It was nightfall and they were tired and hungry. It is said that they asked for hospitality at Luss and were refused, which is a very unusual thing in the Highlands! So, because they were angry as well as hungry, they killed and roasted a black sheep with a white tail. Then they ate their supper and spent the night in a tumble-down barn near Luss. In the morning, of course, the sheep was missed, and its skin was found in the barn beside the two MacGregors. The Colquhouns were so enraged that they hanged both men ; and so began a Clan feud which lasted for nearly a century. Then the Chief of the MacGregors thought it was time to stop the bickering which continually went on, and he went with a following to Luss—to propose peace. But his mission had no result, so the MacGregors took the road for home. The Luss men followed and caught them up at a lonely glen where a terrible fight took place. The MacGregors were the victors. Over two hundred Colquhouns

were killed. The glen is known as Glen Fruin—
the Glen of Weeping.

The Laird of Luss, furious at his defeat, sent a
very unfair account of the business to the King.
His messenger was accompanied by a procession of
widows of the slain Colquhouns, each one mounted
on a white pony and carrying her husband's blood-
stained shirt on the point of a lance. Naturally
this parade made a great impression at Stirling, and
there was no one about the Court to plead the cause
of the MacGregors and urge that the quarrel had
not been of their seeking. The Privy Council
ordered that the name of MacGregor should be
abolished, and that any who continued to bear it
should be put to the sword. The Earl of Argyll
was given authority to hunt and persecute the Clan.
Many MacGregors were killed, and their lands were
seized and given to other Clans. And many went
to different parts of the country and took other
names. But nothing could break the *spirit* of the
Clan! At last a champion arose among them who
thought that he might avenge their wrongs. This
was Robert MacGregor Campbell, or Rob Roy, a
man of good descent. He was a successful cattle
drover who did good business at the Lowland and
Border fairs. The Duke of Montrose advanced a
good deal of money to him to invest in cattle. Un-
fortunately Rob Roy had a dishonest partner who
made off with his money, as well as £1000 belonging

to the Duke, and left Rob to take the blame. The Duke demanded his money back, but Rob had no hope of finding £1000 ! In his predicament he did the worst possible thing, for he took to flight. Then the Duke had his property seized and a warrant issued for his arrest. And from that time onward his life was that of an outlaw, and his daring escapades were the talk of the whole of Britain.

He had many hiding-places. One of them was the very same cave which, four hundred years before, had sheltered Robert the Bruce. Another was a cavern in a mass of rock which rises from Loch Lomond. It is called Rob Roy's Prison, because he used to keep captives there from whom he hoped to extort ransom. His way of dealing with his prisoners was to lower them into the Loch by a rope, and between dips to ask them whether they were ready to agree to his terms ! Several times he was himself captured. Once the Duke of Atholl decoyed him (under pretence of friendship) to his castle, and there Rob was handed over to an officer and sixty soldiers. He let himself be taken quietly, but he made a request that he should be allowed to send a message to his wife. A mounted messenger came to get the message and Rob asked him to dismount, that he might give it to him privately. Unsuspecting, the man got off his horse and Rob began to speak confidentially to him, edging gradually towards the door. Then suddenly he made a spring, and was up, and *off* before anyone could stop him! Another time he was surprised and taken prisoner by the Duke of Montrose, and was bound on a horse behind one of the Duke's followers. It was late evening and growing dark when they reached the River Forth. As they were crossing it the buckle of the girth which bound him slipped, and down Rob dropped into the water and swam for safety, easily getting away in the dark. You can imagine how angry Montrose was when the luckless follower arrived at the river bank without his prisoner!

After many years of wild adventures and amazing escapes Rob Roy settled down to a more or less peaceful life. The Duke of Montrose became less hard on the MacGregors and even began to lease land to them, and Rob went to Balquhidder and settled down to farming. But his proud spirit was never broken—as Sir Walter Scott in his introduction to his novel, *Rob Roy*, tells. He says: " When he was old and ill he was told that a man with whom he had been at enmity in old days was coming to visit him. His pride rose in arms and he said, ' Raise me from my bed, throw my plaid round me and bring me my claymore, dirk and pistols. It shall never be said that a foeman saw Rob Roy defenceless and unarmed ! ' The visitor entering asked after Rob's health and Rob replied civilly though coolly. But as soon as the man had gone he fell back, completely exhausted with the effort.

ROB ROY IN HIDING

' Now,' he said, ' all is over. Let the piper play
Ha til mi tulidh (" We return no more "). Before
the dirge was finished the great Rob Roy was dead."

Late in the eighteenth century a law was passed
allowing the MacGregors to use their name once
more. There have been a great many distinguished
sons of the Clan since then, and Sir Walter Scott's
words have come true, that, after all their misfortunes,
" MacGregor, despite them, shall flourish for ever ! "

VII

CLAN FORBES

CULLODEN—FOR THE KING

PITSLIGO—FOR THE PRINCE

JOHN OF FORBES was the first of the Clan
to be mentioned in Scottish records and that
was in the days of William the Lion. Among
his descendants was Sir John Forbes of that ilk, who
lived in the reigns of Robert II and Robert III. He
had four stalwart sons, and they founded the families
of Forbes of Pitsligo, Waverton, and Foveran in
Aberdeenshire, and of Culloden in Inverness-shire.
James I raised the eldest of these sons to the Peerage
as a reward for distinguished service in France.

A curious custom existed at that time by which a Peer could demand what was called a bond of *man-rent* from a less powerful neighbour. This was a sort of personal bondage. It gave him the right to claim three armed horsemen as a bodyguard " to shield him against all mortals, the King excepted," and this claim Lord Forbes made on the family of Ogston of that ilk. Lord Forbes' wife was the grand-daughter of Robert III, so the Forbeses can boast of royal blood. His branch of the family added considerably to the honours and possessions of the Clan ; and it has always been said that about one-third of the ancient castles in Aberdeenshire were either built by the Forbeses or were at one time owned by them. They were a sturdy race of fighters and saw to it that no one should defraud them of their rights and privileges.

John, the sixth Lord, had a feud with the city of Aberdeen. This town demanded blackmail of a tun of wine for the privilege of the fishings in the River Don, which ran through Forbes land. (A tun is a huge cask which holds 232 gallons.) In 1526 a great fight between the Forbeses and the citizens of Aberdeen took place in the streets. It went on for twenty-four hours without break until both sides were completely exhausted.

The Forbeses of Tolquhoun—like their descendants of Culloden—were ever loyal to the reigning monarch. In the Scots array at the Battle of Worcester one of them commanded a troop of cavalry. When Charles II's horse was shot from under him and it was clear that the fight was going against him, Forbes mounted the King on his own horse, putting also his buff-coloured coat and blood-stained scarf upon the King. Disguised in this way, and surrounded by sixty Forbeses, Charles managed to evade capture, and at nightfall he got away to a safe place and thence to France.

The most famous descendant of this branch was Duncan Forbes of Culloden, the Lord President of the Court of Session. The Government was undoubtedly indebted to him for influencing the northern Highlands against joining in the Rising of the " 'Forty-five." Apart from his loyalty to the Government, he wanted to prevent his friends and neighbours in the north from joining in a cause which he knew very well was doomed to fail. Whenever the news of the raising of Prince Charlie's Standard reached him, he hurried to Inverness and used every means possible to keep the chiefs from going out. He advanced £2000 out of his own pocket for purposes of defence, and the ungrateful Government never repaid him ! While he was acting in this way, one of his kindred in Aberdeenshire, urged equally by conscience and by loyalty—loyalty to the ancient House of Stewart—decided to throw in his lot with Prince Charlie. This was Alex Forbes, Lord Pitsligo, who had always been a recognised leader among the east-country Jacobites. He had fought in the " 'Fifteen," when Prince Charlie's father tried to gain the throne of Scotland. Then, when the next call came—thirty years later—he was an old man of sixty-seven and he naturally hesitated about taking up arms. But not for long! Like the " Gentle Lochiel," he stood firm to the cause, and cheerfully sacrificing his fortunes, placed his life in peril, because of his personal attachment to the House of Stewart. After the defeat of Culloden, when he became an exile and a wanderer, he managed to find shelter in Buchan, a district of north-east Aberdeenshire, on the borders of his own estates. Pitsligo Castle (now a crumbling ruin) stands on rising ground on the north coast in bleak country, whose only attraction is its fine rocky coastline, with —here and there—lovely little sandy bays. Among the rocks near the castle is a cave which was Lord Pitsligo's hiding-place for some years. In a rough recess at its farther end on a shelf of rock dried bracken was laid to serve as bed. Whenever it was safe to do so, his friends brought him food, but he was often reduced to feeding on water-brose—which is just oatmeal moistened with water. He had a few books and they were his only distraction from the cries of the seabirds and the roar of the waves upon the rocky shore. Sometimes he went about the country disguised as a beggar. Lady Pitsligo used to sew bags for him with which to go about collect-

E

ing meal and broken meats. Another hiding-place was under the arch of a small bridge near Fraserburgh. Sometimes he was taken by surprise. On one occasion a patrol of soldiers came upon him near Rosehearty and, taking him for a genuine beggar, commanded him to " take them to the cave where Lord Pitsligo was in hiding ! " He could not help himself and he led them to his own rocky cavern. He was amused at the precautions they took to avoid warning its hoped-for occupant. They tiptoed among the rocks, and bursting into the cave shouted, " In the King's name, surrender ! " But only the echoes answered : and the seabirds, indignant at the intruders, screamed shrilly, and attacked their faces with wings and beaks, so that the soldiers had to retreat. Owing to the cold and exposure, Lord Pitsligo became a victim to asthma. One day he had a bad fit of coughing at the roadside, during which a patrol passed. So little did the soldiers suspect him that one of them stopped and sympathised with him and even gave him a small sum of money !

In this way his life went on for ten long years, and meanwhile his title and estates had been forfeited by law. His last escape was a very strange one. A rumour had reached the commanding officer in Fraserburgh that the old man was hiding a few miles away in the House of Auchiries, where his son lived. A lady who was visiting in the house dreamed re-

peatedly one night that soldiers surrounded the
house, and her dream was so persistent that she got
up and looked out of the window. Dawn was just
breaking, and to her amazement she saw soldiers
posted round the house as she had seen them in her
dream. She gave the alarm at once, and the family
lost no time in transferring the old man from his
bed to a recess behind the panelled walls of one of
the bedrooms. A bed was placed against this panel
and the lady who had dreamed lay down in it before
the soldiers were admitted. They searched every
corner of the house. The lady's bed was carefully
examined, and the soldiers even felt her chin to
make sure that she was not a man in a woman's
nightgown! While they were doing this the stuffy
air of the recess brought on poor Lord Pitsligo's
cough, and his breathing became so loud that those
in the house were terrified for his safety. But the
lady was equal to the occasion. She coughed so
loudly and violently herself that she succeeded in
covering the noise which he made, and the soldiers
departed discomfited. When Lord Pitsligo could
speak after being released from his uncomfortable
hiding-place, he said kindly to his servant—" James,
go and see that those poor fellows get some breakfast and a drink of warm ale. It is a cold morning
and they are only doing their duty." And he added
with a smile, " A poor prize, had they got me—an
old dying man ! " No further attempt was made to

seize him and he lived on with his son until the age of eighty-five.

The Forbeses may well be proud of this clansman of theirs, for his character was worthy of remembrance. It was said of him by a great man of his day : " I have never heard this gentleman speak an ill word of any man living ; but I have always observed him ready to defend any other person who was ill spoken of in his company. My Lord Pitsligo will always find good in everybody." Aytoun's ballad rightly calls him :

" The good old Scottish Cavalier
All of the olden time."

VIII

CLAN MENZIES

AMONG those families which were not origi-
inally Highland, but have won both power
and position in the Highlands, is that of
Menzies.

The clansfolk are of Celtic stock, but the head
of the family is generally believed to have come over
from Normandy with William the Conqueror, and
to have the same root as the English family of
Manners, of the Rutland dukedom. The name was
then " de Menyers," and so it was written in early
Scottish records, when the family seat was at Duris-
deer in Nithsdale. Since that time it has been spelt
in many different ways. The reason for introducing

Z into its present form has always been a puzzle, but a possible clue is given in the *Red and White Book of Menzies*.

In ancient times, when scarcely anybody but the monks could read and write, all letters and documents were written by professional scribes. The letter Z in Latin writing was so remarkably like the Celtic G that it is probable that the writer of some important document used it in error. There would be no one to correct the mistake, and the spelling would be repeated in succeeding documents as MENZIES. That, of course, would not affect the pronunciation which has always been " Mingis." Whether correct or not, that is the theory of the Menzies Chronicler.

The Menzieses of the thirteenth century were a very able family. In 1249 Lord Robert de Menyers was Lord High Chancellor of Scotland. He was often sent on embassies to the English Court, and his conduct of affairs was of great advantage to both nations. In his time Scotland made great progress in Commerce, Literature and the Arts. His son got a grant of the lands of Weem, Aberfeldy, and Glendochart from Robert the Bruce ; and his grandson was given land in Fortingall by Robert II. His family must always have been in favour with royalty, for grants of land to different branches were given, in counties as far apart as Peebles, Lothian and Aberdeen,—where they took a prominent part in civic government.

In the sixteenth century the Menzieses came into serious conflict with their Highland neighbours. After three generations there was no male heir to Fortingall and the estate went to the Stewarts, by marriage with the Menzies heiress. Then Menzies of Weem laid claim to the lands of Rannoch and was granted a charter of them by James IV. The very day the charter was signed, the wild men of Rannoch descended upon Weem. They were led by Neil Stewart, a kinsman of the Menzieses by marriage ; and besides doing a great deal of damage they burned down Castle Weem. Such an affront had, of course, to be avenged, so the Menzieses in full force promptly burned down Stewart's Castle of Garth ! Apart from the destruction of two fine old castles, the loss to the Menzies family was very great, because with Castle Weem were burnt all the early records of their origin, besides several important royal charters. To judge from the stories that have been passed on by word of mouth in Perthshire it would seem that the Menzies chiefs were settled at Weem much earlier than is shown by existing history. There is an ancient Gaelic ballad about an ogre who in very early ages lived in a cave—or Pict's house—at Weem. He went about in the guise of a monk with a scarlet cowl, and his fierce and repulsive appearance terrified the whole neighbourhood. One day he met the daughter of the Menzies Chief. She was a girl of great beauty and " His Ogreship "

determined to have her for his bride. She fled
from him in horror, but he accomplished his fell
purpose and carried her off to his cave. She was
never seen again !

A belief exists among the Clan that Crinan, Abbot
of Dunkeld, was a Menzies chief. He married the
daughter of King Malcolm II, and their son Duncan
became King of Scotland. Duncan was assassinated
by Macbeth, Thane of Cawdor, who usurped the
crown and occupied the throne of Scotland for
seventeen years. Everybody knows the story of
Macbeth consulting three witches as to his prospects,
and how they told him that until Birnam Wood
should come to Dunsinane he ·should never be
conquered or lose his crown. In time Duncan's
son, Malcolm, came to manhood, and he raised an
army to attack Macbeth and avenge his father.
This army (which included Menzieses in full strength)
spent the night before the attack in Birnam Woods.
Early in the morning Malcolm ordered that every
man should hew down a branch and bear it before
him on the march to Dunsinane, where Macbeth's
stronghold was. So hidden, the strength of his
army could not possibly be estimated by the enemy
in the fort. When told by a sentinel of the strange
appearance of the advancing wood, Macbeth wrath-
fully refused to believe him. But " seeing is believing " and Macbeth's incredulity was changed to
terror when he realised that his doom was about

MACBETH AND THE WITCHES

to overtake him—as indeed turned out to be the case ! Malcolm's success in this battle restored the old royal line of Scotland, which lasted without a break for hundreds of years. In the advance of Birnam Wood the Menzieses carried branches of the rowan (or mountain-ash) which, ever since, has been the Clan badge. Their hunting tartan also repeats the colours of the rowan-tree—green for the leaves and scarlet for the berries.

Another tree which will always be associated with a Menzies is the larch ; for, from the Austrian Tyrol, Menzies of Culdares brought in his portmanteau the first larches ever planted in Scotland. This was in 1737. The Duke of Atholl of that time was a skilful and enthusiastic gardener—he was called " The Planting Duke." Menzies presented the Duke with some of the young larches and they were planted at Dunkeld. Two of them can be seen—now grown to monstrous size—beside Dunkeld Cathedral. They proved to be ideally suitable for the Scottish climate and soil, and seedlings were begged—or even stolen—by gardeners from all over the kingdom.

At Castle Menzies there are some of the finest trees in all Scotland. When Prince Charlie's father came to Britain in 1715 to make a bid for the throne of Scotland, the Menzieses were among the Clans which rallied to his call—as the following verse of a poem by Campbell tells :

" Wha' will ride wi' gallant Murray ?
Wha' will ride wi' Geordie's sel' ?
He's the flow'r o' a' Glenisla
An' the darling o' Dunkell !
Menzies, he's our friend and brother,
Gask and Strowan are nae slack ;
Noble Perth has ta'en the field,
And a' the Drummonds at his back ! "

But, as you know, this rising ended in failure. When, thirty years later, the attractive—but just as unfortunate—Stewart Prince Charles Edward came over on the same errand as his father, Menzies of Culdares did not himself turn out ; but his clansmen did, under Menzies of Shian. Prince Charlie spent two happy days at Castle Menzies, not long before his mission failed on the field of Culloden. He had some good hunting and, for the time, cast all his cares to the winds of Perthshire.

Although Menzies did not join the Rising, he showed his sympathy by sending a very handsome charger to the Prince for his own use. The horse was taken by one of the clansmen and was to be handed over to Prince Charlie who was then in England. But on the way south both man and horse were captured by Government troops. The man was pressed to reveal the name of the sender of the horse, and was told that, if he did, he should go free. But the loyal Highlander would not betray his chief ; he preferred—and suffered—death, which was the only alternative offered him.

Ben Lawers, one of the highest Perthshire mountains, is partly on Weem territory. It is a very beautiful hill and on it are found many rare plants. A story is told of a St. Andrews professor who wanted to climb the mountain. He asked the Menzies Chief to give him an escort for that purpose, and a gillie was told off to show the way. As they ascended the mountain the professor exclaimed—loud and often—at the rare plants, the glorious views, the fine air, and what not—until the gillie was thoroughly tired of his companion's enthusiasm. At last they reached the summit and, as the professor's eyes travelled from one range of mountains to another, he exclaimed in delight, " Isn't this *marvellous* ! Tell me, have any living beings ever been here before ? " And the gillie dourly said, " Oh, well indeed, sir, there's plenty goats come up Ben Lawers." That day, it is said, a quiet and thoughtful professor went down Ben Lawers !

IX

CLAN MACKINTOSH

THE Gaelic word t-o-i-s-i-c-h (" tosh ") means thane or earl, and some historians say that the first Mackintosh was the son of MacDuff, Thane or Earl of Fife.

For centuries Clan Mackintosh was prominent in the north-east Highlands, and when the Chief became the acknowledged captain of Clan Chattan as well, its importance was greatly enhanced.

The family seat of the Mackintosh is Moy Hall, on the banks of Loch Moy in Inverness-shire. There have been no fewer than three castles at Moy. What remains of the first is on an island in the loch ; the second—which for a short time sheltered Prince Charlie—was burnt down; and the third—where King George sometimes visited—was built late in the eighteenth century.

Clan Chattan was the name of a combine of nine or ten Clans, which in early times banded themselves together in order to keep a grip of the north-east counties. The two leading Clans in this combine were Mackintosh and Macpherson, and there was between these two a good deal of rivalry.

But the members of Clan Chattan were just like the members of some large family. They might—and *did*—quarrel among themselves, but if an outsider began to make trouble with any one of them the rest at once rose in his defence.

For example, Mackintosh of Moy had come to loggerheads with an old enemy, Macdonald of Keppoch. In a fierce fight at Mulroy the Moy men had the worst of it, and their Chief was taken prisoner.

That was a black day for the Mackintosh!

But before the Macdonalds could collect their scattered forces, warpipes were heard, and, to their dismay, a large body of Macphersons appeared in full battle array. They sent a message to Macdonald that, unless he was prepared for another fight, he must deliver up the Mackintosh at once!

A *second* battle in one day! Alas! No! Not even the Macdonalds could face that, so ruefully they had to hand over their prize. And the Macphersons, in triumph, escorted the Mackintosh Chief back to his estate of Moy !

Clan Comyn also had an old-standing feud with the Mackintoshes. On one occasion this Clan managed to drive the Mackintoshes to take refuge on the Island of Moy, and afterwards started making a dam, so as to raise the level of the loch and flood the island.

The Mackintoshes would certainly have been drowned had not one of their number gone down at dead of night and bored a number of holes in the wood which lined the dam. In each hole he placed a plug with a string attached, then all the strings were fastened to one rope. When everything was ready the Mackintoshes gave the main rope a mighty pull, and out came all the plugs !

The banked-up water poured through the holes with a fearful force, carrying away the wood, the turf which banked it up, *and* the Comyns who were encamped behind it !

For a long time the Chiefs of Mackintosh were associated with a dreadful curse. The story is told in an old poem called *The Curse of Moy*. A Mackintosh Chief wanted to marry Margaret, daughter of a Grant Chief. Margaret refused his proposal because she was already engaged to Grant of Alva— and great was the affront to the Mackintosh ! But he was determined not to be baulked, and he captured not only the lady, but her father and lover as well, and imprisoned all three in the island castle. Poor Margaret wept, and begged for mercy from her captor, who agreed to spare *one* of his prisoners, leaving her to choose which should die!

Margaret's father prevailed upon her to choose her lover's freedom, but that did not please Mackintosh at all, and in his rage he killed both men, and confronted the poor girl with their bodies! The poem tells how she went out of her mind, and for years roamed about among the Badenoch mountains.

Over a cairn built in memory of her father and her lover she called down a curse on their murderer, praying that he might die childless:

" That never the son of a Chief of Moy
    Might live to protect his father's age,
  Or close in peace his dying eye,
    Or gather his gloomy heritage."

And superstitious folks looked upon it as the fulfilment of the curse, that for over a hundred years no Chief of Mackintosh left a son to succeed him. But with Angus, the twenty-fifth Chief, the spell was broken, for his son and his grandson in turn became Chief of the Clan.

In reading the history of any of the great Clans, one sees them constantly striving for supremacy over their powerful neighbours. The Mackintoshes, for instance, had to keep a watchful eye on Moray and Banffshire. Even far-away Ross-shire held possible enemies.

One of the worst Clan fights on record took place between the Mackintoshes and the Munros of Foulis, over the division of plunder taken by the Munros from a Perthshire Clan. They met at Clachnaharry, near Inverness, and scarcely any of the combatants were left to tell the tale !

Soon after William, the sixth Chief, became head of the Clan he was involved in the renewal of an old family quarrel with the Marquis of Huntly.

How it originated we do not know, but at this time young Mackintosh burned down the Castle of Auchindown. Huntly marched against him, and a fierce battle ensued in which William was taken prisoner. He was tried in Aberdeen, and condemned to death by a Court selected by Huntly.

The only man who dared to protest was Menzies, Provost of Aberdeen, and he was so incensed by the unfairness of the trial that he announced his intention of reporting it to Parliament. Even Huntly did not dare to proceed with the sentence, but he sent Mackintosh to the care of Lady Huntly at his Castle of Strathbogie.

The young man appealed to her for justice, and (according to Sir Walter Scott) she replied to him, " Mackintosh, you have offended Huntly so deeply that he has sworn that he will never pardon you until he has brought your neck to the block."

This interview took place in the kitchen of Strathbogie and William loosened his collar, and laid his head on the wooden block on which cattle and sheep were broken up, saying, as he did so, " Even to that humiliation I will stoop, to secure the safety of my father's house ! " A generous-hearted woman would have been touched by such submission, but not so the Marchioness ! She made a sign to the cook, who was standing near with a meat chopper in his hand, and he raised it and struck off the young man's head !

Another—but very different—woman to bear a share in Clan affairs was Lady Mackintosh at the time of the " 'Forty-five."

Although only twenty at the time, she was so active in Prince Charlie's service that she became known as " Colonel Anne." Her husband was out on the Government side with Loudon's High-landers, but she was a Farquharson of Invercauld and therefore a devoted Jacobite. In order to help the Prince she roused her husband's Clan to sympathetic action, and a strong, well-armed battalion was formed. On the battalion's first appearance " Colonel Anne " reviewed them, with a man's bonnet on her head, a tartan riding-habit, and pistols at her saddle-bow !

In February 1746—just after visiting the Menzies at Weem Castle—Prince Charlie came to Moy. The night he arrived, Lady Mackintosh sent out the

blacksmith of Moy, with four other men, to guard
the approach from Inverness against sudden alarm.
It was a wild night of thunder and lightning and the
scouts took up position beside a number of peat
stacks which were drying on both sides of the road.
Presently they heard approaching the regular tramp
of marching troops. They were five men against
hundreds—what could they do ? When the soldiers
came near the blacksmith and his men began rushing
about among the peat-stacks, firing their guns and
shouting loudly the war-cries of Lochiel, Keppoch,
and other well-known Jacobite Clans.

The lightning lit up the peat-stacks, which to the
soldiers looked like bodies of men in formation, and
they thought that the Jacobite army was upon them
in full strength. They hesitated, broke, and fled
back to Inverness as hard as they could go ! And
so ended what is known as the " Rout of Moy."

The gallant smith was ever after known as
" Captein nan Coig " (" Captain of the Five ").
He was made an officer in the Mackintosh Regiment,
and his sword was preserved in the district. His
anvil is now at Moy Hall, along with several relics of
Prince Charlie.

After Culloden, a party of Government soldiers was
sent to bring Lady Mackintosh to Inverness. Mounted
on the only horse left at Moy she rode with them,
undaunted and unconcerned. She was kept under
guard for six weeks and afterwards set at liberty.

Some years later, at a ball given by the Duke of Cumberland in London, the first tune played was *Up and waur them a', Willie*. It was the tune which was played by the bells of St. Giles, when the Duke passed through Edinburgh on his way to the Highlands, to suppress the Prince Charlie Rising.

To this tune the Duke invited Lady Mackintosh to dance and she could not refuse her host. The dance finished, she said, " Well, sir, I have danced to your tune. Will you now dance to mine ? "

Being always gallant the Duke could not say, " No "; but the victor of Culloden must have felt himself in rather a ridiculous position when he found that the tune which the lady called, and to which he had to dance, was, *The Auld Stuarts back again!* So the final honour in that skirmish went unquestionably to gallant " Colonel Anne ! "

X

CLAN MUNRO

THERE is some uncertainty as to the early home of the Clan Munro—or Clan Roich, as it is in the Gaelic. Some writers say that the Munros came from Ireland in far back ages; that they are descended from Donald O'Ceann, son of the Prince of Fermanagh, who came over to help Malcolm II against Danish invaders; and that Donald's reward was the land to the north-west of the Cromarty Firth which is still known as " Ferin-Donald " (" the Land of Donald "). They say also that the name " Munro " was taken from a river in County Derry called the Roe, and that Foulis (the name of the Munros' family seat) is derived from Loch Foyle, into which the Roe flows.

Whether this be true or not, the Munros have certainly owned their lands in Ross-shire for nearly eight hundred years. We know that they always kept on good terms with their great northern neighbours, the Earls of Sutherland and Ross, for very early in their history a Munro married the Earl of Sutherland's daughter. And, later, the family took a charter of land (they called it a Bond of Kindness and Alliance) from the Earl of Ross.

The land was granted to them on the curious condition that every year they should give the Earl of Ross a pair of white gloves, or three pennies, if required !

Loyalty to the Rosses led to an extraordinary loss in the Munro succession. In the time of Alexander III a rebellion broke out against the Earl of Ross. Its leader was seized and imprisoned at Dingwall, and, in revenge, the rebels went to the Ross Castle of Balnagown, and stole the Earl's son, holding him as a hostage against their imprisoned captain. Pursuit of the rebels by the Munros and Dingwalls ended in a dreadful fight, and although the Ross supporters won, their losses in men were very heavy.

Actually eleven Munros of the House of Foulis— who would naturally have succeeded in turn— fell, so that the only heir left was an infant then in its cradle. But the Earl's son was rescued and borne back in triumph to Balnagown, and that strengthened the good feeling already existing between the Rosses and the Munros.

In the fourteenth century John Munro of Foulis was travelling from Edinburgh to Ross-shire. On the way he and his retinue stopped for a night's rest in a meadow at Strathardle in Perthshire. While they were sleeping, the owner of the meadow came and cut off the tails of their horses.

Such an insult was bound to be avenged as soon as possible, so when Munro reached Foulis, he at once summoned his kinsmen and followers and organised a raid on the offenders. He returned with a large party to Strathardle, and killed some of the inhabitants and drove away their best cattle.

As the victorious party passed through Moy on their way home, the Mackintosh sent a message to Munro demanding *his* share of the spoil. The payment of what was called a " Road Collop " for the liberty of driving plundered cattle through another chief's land was a regular Highland custom, and the Munros offered what they thought was a generous share. But the Mackintosh demanded a half-share and this the Munros refused and went on their way. The Mackintoshes pursuing them overtook them at Clachnaharry, near Inverness, where one of the worst Clan fights on record took place ; in fact both sides were almost wiped out !

Euphemia, daughter of the Earl of Ross, was the

wife of Robert II, and when the eighth Laird of
Foulis married her niece, the Munros became
vassals of the Crown. To hold land from a king
raised the rank of a family. The ceremony itself
was very quaint. When the vassal went into the
King's presence, he fell on his knees and put his
hands into the royal hands, the King then kissing
him on the mouth. At the same time the Munro
took an oath that he would be the King's faithful
vassal all his life; and a charter was then granted
to show that, for all time coming, certain lands would
belong to him and his successors. In the charter
granted by King Robert to the Munros there was
only one condition—that in return for their lands
they should produce for the King a *snowball* at
midsummer! Foulis Castle lies just below Ben
Wyvis in Ross-shire, and on the northern side of
that massive mountain are corries where the snow
never melts, so a " snowball rent " even at midsummer was easy to pay!

In the reign of James VI, Lord Reay and Sir
Robert Munro — commonly called " The Black
Baron "—were the first chiefs to seek military glory
in foreign service.

Munro raised a regiment seven hundred strong
among his own people, and fought, first for the
King of Denmark and later for Prince Gustavus
Adolphus of Sweden.

At one time there were in the Swedish army no

fewer than fifty-seven officers of the name of Munro, not counting subalterns.

The military connection of the Clan was extended to India, where several Munros gained honour and renown. But India took an ungrateful toll of them, for two, at least, came to an untimely end—one being killed by a tiger and another devoured by a shark !

In addition to military distinction the Munros have achieved great things in Statesmanship, and in Literature, Law and Medicine.

Fifteen years after the Chair of Anatomy was founded in Edinburgh University three Monros in succession held the professorship for the long period of 126 years. The earliest of these (who was always spoken of as " Monro Primus ") distinguished himself at the Battle of Prestonpans, not as a slayer but as a healer. He attended to the wounded on both sides, and organised what was really an ambulance corps, to get the wounded taken to Edinburgh for treatment.

He made an interesting bargain with the Edinburgh Town Council which, at that time, appointed the professors. He offered to send his son to be trained at the best medical schools, both at home and abroad, if they would promise to appoint him Professor of Anatomy afterwards. And they had such faith in the father that they agreed to accept the son.

When the young man was fully qualified, he

returned to Edinburgh and Monro Primus invited the City dignitaries to come and listen to his son's first lecture.

Monro Secundus had got it off by heart, but when he found himself faced by such a distinguished audience the poor fellow suddenly lost his nerve and forgot every word of the lecture ! But when he had got over his first fright he pulled himself together, and, knowing his subject so thoroughly, he made a most brilliant oration and justified the faith of the Council. After this experience he never used notes for his lectures during the fifty-four years of his term as Professor of Anatomy. He was succeeded in turn by his son, Monro Tertius.

There is a story told about a Munro of Achany—a Sutherland branch of the Clan. The Earl of Sutherland, early one autumn, issued a commission to William Munro of Achany in Sutherlandshire, who with a large body of retainers and clansmen made a descent on Assynt and carried off a great many cattle. At the end of summer, milk being plentiful, big supplies of butter and cheese had been made and laid in for winter use. So the Munros, not content with the cattle, made a clean sweep, and plundered the shielings of great quantities of butter and cheese as well ! Assynt at one time belonged to Macleod of Lewis, but that family became extinct and the estate passed by marriage to the Mackenzies of Kintail.

In revenge for the raid of the Munros, a song was written and circulated by an Assynt farmer called Macleod, who set his words to the tune of *Caber Feidh*, the Clan March of the Mackenzies.

The song contained very bitter sarcasm about Sutherland and the Munros, who, in turn, were furious at the gibes in it, especially those about the butter and cheese. And Achany vowed that if he ever met the author of the song he would certainly kill him !

They were personally unknown to each other, but Achany was well known by a grey bonnet which he always wore—which had earned for him the name " Uilleam a Bhonaid Aidhir " (" William of the Grey Bonnet ").

One day he entered Ardgay Inn where sat Macleod, who was on his way to Tain Market, refreshing himself with bread and butter, cheese and ale. Macleod at once recognised the grey bonnet, and after the fashion of the day, rose and drank to the stranger, afterwards offering him the horn of ale in his turn. On the spur of the moment, he made up a Gaelic verse which he recited to Munro, and which, translated, ran something like this :

" Bread and butter and cheese for me
　　Ere death my mouth shall close,
And, traveller, there's a drink for thee
　　To please the Black Munros ! "

Achany was gratified at this address and he quaffed the stranger's ale, and then asked his name. When told the name he was very much taken aback— but there !—he had drunk with the Macleod as his guest and he could do nothing but forgive him. And it is pleasant to record that the two were quite good friends ever after !

XI

ROBERTSON—CLAN DONNACHIE

ACCORDING to a famous historian the Robertsons of Struan are the oldest family in Scotland, and the only remaining branch of the royal race which gave kings to the throne of Scotland during the eleventh and twelfth centuries.

The Clan was known from early times as Clan Donnachie, after a Chief called Donnachaidh Reamhar, or Duncan the Stout.

Robert the Bruce was very friendly with one of the Chiefs of Clan Donnachie, who, by request of the Bruce, took the name of Robert. The son of this Chief did not use the Gaelic " Mac," but was called " Robert, Son of Robert," so the family name became Robertson. When a Clan was marching to battle, a standard-bearer carrying the Clan banner always led the way. One night when Clan Donnachie was on the way to Bannockburn to help Bruce, the Clan banner was as usual laid near its bearer on the ground. And when he lifted the standard in the morning a precious stone which looked like a ball of milky crystal was found adhering to it. This incident was of course looked upon by Clan Donnachie as a sign that Fortune would be with them in the fight. They called the stone "Clach-nan-Brattich"—or "Stone of the Banner"— and had it fixed to the top of the standard pole, and they never afterwards went into battle without it.

The Robertsons were always very loyal supporters of the Stewart kings. Indeed their crest is taken from an incident connected with James I of Scotland who was murdered in Blackfriars Monastery in Perth in the year 1451.

The Chief of the Clan followed the murderers and captured them in a lonely glen in Atholl. In recognition of this service his lands were made into a barony and to his coat-of-arms was added a crest which shows a hand and arm holding up a royal crown, and a savage in chains hanging from the shield. The motto granted to the Chief was "*Virtutis Gloria Merces*" ("Glory is the reward of Valour"). One of the most famous of Robertson chiefs was Alexander, who was, almost certainly, the only chief in Scotland who was out in all three Jacobite Risings. In 1688, along with Graham of Claverhouse, he fought on the Stuart side, and had to take refuge in France. Queen Anne granted him a pardon and he returned to Scotland. Then came the Rising in 1715, when with five hundred of his clansmen he was at the Raising of the Standard on the Braes of Mar; he afterwards fought at Sheriffmuir. Twice he was taken prisoner and rescued; the second time, with the help of his sister, he escaped the Government soldiers and got away safely to France.

When the Rebellion of the " 'Forty-five " broke out he was seventy-five years old, but he insisted on joining his Clan and fighting for Prince Charlie at the Battle of Prestonpans. The Jacobite leaders, with some difficulty, persuaded him to go home and leave the rest of the fighting to the younger men.

Once persuaded, he must have quite enjoyed his journey, for it was made in a very grandly fitted-up carriage which had been captured from Sir John Cope. When the party reached the wilds of Rannoch, and the roads became too bad for carriage-wheels, the clansmen simply carried the carriage, their Chief within it, to his family residence, which was just below the great mountain Schiehallion. The old Highlanders must have been a sturdy race, for an old-fashioned carriage was no light weight!

Alexander Robertson was a scholar as well as a

soldier. He was known as "The Poet Chief," and after his death a volume of poems written by him was published. "Baron Bradwardine," a character in Sir Walter Scott's novel, *Waverley*, is said to be a portrait of him. The talent for poetry was inherited by another of the race, for Baroness Nairne, the famous writer of many well-known Scots songs, was descended from the Robertsons of Struan. *The Auld Hoose*, one of her best-known songs, was written about the House of Gask, which belonged to her people. The old house became so dilapidated as to be unsafe and a new house was built close by into which the family moved. Lady Nairne's grandfather, Duncan Robertson of Struan, insisted that the last article taken from the old house to the new one should be the Family Bible, and he asked that he might have the honour of carrying it. Just as he had crossed the threshold with his precious burden the door of the "Auld Hoose" burst its hinges and fell heavily outwards and the Chief had a very narrow escape!

For nearly five hundred years a branch of the Robertson family had a property in Perthshire called Lude. A greatly prized heirloom belonged to these Robertsons, who, like their Struan relatives, were keen supporters of the Stuarts. This was a harp which once belonged to Mary Queen of Scots.

The Queen stayed at Atholl in 1564, and an old record tells that a kind of competition amongst the

G

native harpers was held in her honour. At this festival she adjudged the victory to Beatrix Gardyn of Banchory, to whom she gave her own harp as a prize. Beatrix Gardyn married one of the Robertsons of Lude and the harp was handed down in that family. Later it passed into the possession of a Stewart of Dalguise, and it was re-strung and actually played upon in the nineteenth century.

Music was an inherited talent among the Robertsons. Charles Robertson of Auchleeks (another connection) was so skilful a harper that he was known all over Perthshire as " Charles of the Strings." He married Beatrix Robertson of Lude—a descendant of the Beatrix Gardyn to whom Queen Mary gave her harp. Music in Scotland is deeply indebted to a descendant of the Robertson family, for he founded the Chair of Music in Edinburgh University.

He was General John Reid, the son of Alexander Robertson of Straloch, whose forefathers for over three hundred years were always called Barons Rua, Roy, or Red, because the family had red hair. The head of the family always signed himself " Robertson " until the General's time. He did not observe the rule, but kept the name and signature of " Red," which he changed later on to " Reid." He had great taste for music and was one of the best flute-players of his time. When he was major in the 42nd Regiment he set the words of *The Garb of Old*

Gaul to music, and this composition has ever since been the Regimental March. He left £52,000 for the purpose of establishing a Professorship of Music in the University of Edinburgh where he was educated. By his will he appointed that on or about the 13th of January (the date of his birthday) an annual concert should be held in the Hall of the Professor of Music and that the programme should commence with one of his compositions and include *The Garb of Old Gaul*. That was how the Reid Concerts began, and at the present day each January Concert opens with *The Garb of Old Gaul* and the audience rises to honour the memory of the man who did so much for music in Scotland.

Although Perth is the home county of Clan Donnachie many branches are settled in other counties—particularly in Aberdeenshire, Ross-shire and Lanarkshire and several variations of the name are found. These include Duncanson and Mac-Robbie. In Aberdeenshire some of the Clan took the name of Duncan, others that of MacConnachie, which was derived from Conan, the grandfather of Duncan the Stout.

The gathering-place of the Clan in olden times was the Fea Coire, a lonely glen behind the Rannoch Mountains.

XII

CLAN GORDON

THE Gordons are generally classed as a north country Clan because, for centuries, they have owned large tracts of land in the north-east of Scotland. But actually they had lands in Berwickshire and the Borders long before they settled in the north.

Some writers say that their ancestors came from France, from the village of Gourdon in Normandy.

The story is that the first Gordon to cross Tweed was a friend of Malcolm Canmore. He had the reputation of being a very valiant knight, and it is said that by his skill as a hunter he was able to rid Tweedside of a monstrous wild boar which had ravaged the whole district, killing many of the inhabitants. His bravery was rewarded by a grant of land in the district, and to commemorate his deed the boar's head was assumed as the armorial bearings of the family.

For three hundred years the Clan was closely connected with the history of the Borders. When the head of the family moved to the north the Gordons of Lochinvar and the Gordons of Earlston remained to carry on the name in the south of Scotland.

Early in their history a Gordon was killed while fighting in the Crusades. His grandson helped William Wallace to recapture the Castle of Wigton, of which he was made governor; and as a reward for his many faithful services, Robert the Bruce gave him a charter of the district of Strathbogie—or Huntly—in Aberdeenshire. It consisted of about a hundred and twenty square miles of land.

In 1388 the Earl of Douglas led a picked army into the north of England to fight the great Earl of Northumberland. There is an old ballad about the event which is called *The Battle of Otterbourne*, in which the name of the Gordons appears. The ballad begins:

> " It fell about the Lammas tide
> When the muir men win their hay,
> The doughty Earl of Douglas rode
> Into England to catch a prey."

Then three Clans specially chosen to help him are mentioned. It continues :

> " *He chose the Gordons* and the Graemes,
>   With them the Lindsays light and gay—"

It is unnecessary to quote many stanzas, but later comes the following :

> " The moon was clear, the day drew near,
>   The spears in flinders flew,
> But mony a gallant Englishman
>   Ere day the Scotsmen slew."
> The Gordons good in English blood
>   They steeped their hose and shoon."

So the Gordons must have fought very lustily ! But it was not only English blood that was spilt that moonlight night, for the leader of the Gordons was killed. His son, Sir Adam Gordon, it is related, gave his life for his country.

The great-grandson of the Otterbourne Gordon was created Earl of Huntly in recognition of his public service. Honour succeeded honour, for, some generations later, a descendant was made Marquis of Huntly ; and the fourth Marquis became Duke of Gordon.

Two regiments called the Gordon Highlanders have been raised from this Clan, and both have earned the highest distinction in every war in which they have fought. When the second of these regi-

ments was being raised, the Duchess of Gordon of
that time had a method of her own for helping the
recruiting. She promised that each recruit who took
the King's shilling should have a kiss along with it ;
and a kiss from a beautiful duchess proved to be an
irresistible inducement to the lads of the north-east !

In the sixteenth century one of the Gordons of
Aboyne married Elizabeth, Countess of Sutherland.
That established the name in the Highlands, for
the Earls of Sutherland took the surname of Gordon
and used it for more than two hundred years before
they revived their old family name.

In East Aberdeenshire the Gordons are represented by the Earls of Aberdeen. Lord Byron,
the poet, was descended from the Gordons of Gight
in the same district. There are several branches of
the Clan in Morayshire and the Laird of one of them
was at one time a much-talked-of person. He was
Sir Robert Gordon, and was known as the " Warlock
Laird of Moray." He must have made a study of
chemistry, because he had a laboratory in his house
of Gordonstown, and it is said the queer old tools
and crucibles and chemical apparatus that he used
are still in existence. He was believed by the
country folks to have uncanny powers, and stories
are told about his weird doings. It was said that
he had been trained as a sorcerer and that he had
sold his shadow to the devil in payment of his
knowledge of wizardry !

The Lairds of Gordonstown apparently found it convenient to be " Not at Home " to callers at times, for in the old house there are several secret hiding-places which are very carefully arranged. One is gained by the removal in one of the rooms of two planks, when a secret stair is disclosed, leading to a hidden room. Another secret stair leads to the roof, and behind a cupboard is a recess large enough to hold half a dozen people.

A good deal of smuggling in those days went on in the north-east coast of Morayshire. It was not a particularly difficult matter because part of the coast is simply honeycombed with caves. One cave, which can be reached only at high tide, has the date 1650 on its walls. It is said to have been the smuggling stronghold of the Warlock Laird. He had a little brig called the *Nancy* and when a cargo of contraband goods was expected from France, her skipper used to watch for certain signals which told that she must be ready to take over from the French vessel. After the transfer, the goods were hidden in the cave until a high tide at night allowed of their safe removal. Another cave was used as a stable by a later Gordon of Gordonstown. In this cave he hid his horses in case they should be " borrowed " by the Jacobite soldiers. Needless to say, once borrowed they were unlikely to be returned ! Of the southern Gordons the Lochinvar branch was the best known. Sir Walter Scott wrote a poem which was possibly founded on a romantic incident in the Lochinvar family. A young Gordon in days of old was in love with the daughter of Graeme of Netherby in Cumberland. The young lady returned his affection, but her father refused to consider the offer of the young Scotsman and he arranged another marriage for her. Hearing at the last moment that the wedding day was fixed and the date close at hand, young Lochinvar rode off at full speed into England to try and stop it. But when he arrived at Netherby the wedding festivities were in full swing. Nothing daunted, he claimed the right to drink a cup of wine and tread the measure of a dance with the bride. However annoyed they might feel, neither her father, mother, nor bridegroom could refuse him the privilege. So the young couple danced together to the admiration of the assembled guests. Then :

"One touch to her hand, and one word in her
    ear,
  When they reached the hall door and the
    charger stood near.
  So light to the croupe the fair lady he swung,
  So light to the saddle before her he sprung.
  She is won ! We are gone, over bank, bush
    and scaur !
  'They'll have fleet steeds that follow,' quoth
    young Lochinvar !

> There was mounting 'mong Graemes of the
>   Netherby Clan,
> Fosters, Fenwicks and Musgraves, they rode
>   and they ran.
> There was racing and chasing on Canonbie
>   Lee,
> But the lost bride of Netherby ne'er did they
>   see !
> So daring in love and so dauntless in war,
> Have ye e'er heard of gallant like young
>   Lochinvar ? "

In the time of Charles I a member of the Lochinvar family was created Viscount Kenmure. This title was forfeited at the Stewart Rebellion of 1715. The Viscount Kenmure of that day was captured at the Battle of Preston, carried to London, tried, condemned and beheaded. On the scaffold he expressed regret that he had not thought of providing himself with a black suit so that he might have died with more decency ! And before laying his head on the block he presented his executioner with eight guineas !

The greatest Gordon within living memory was Charles George Gordon, the hero of Khartoum. He joined the army in his youth and fought with distinction in the Crimean War. Six years later he put an end to a terrible rebellion which broke out in China. He commanded an army of British

and Americans, and with them he won thirty-three
battles in succession. He refused to take any
reward for his services although the Emperor of
China offered him enormous sums of money. Later,
as Governor of the Egyptian Equatorial Provinces,
he worked hard to put down the Slave Trade. In
1884, being then Governor of the Soudan, he
returned after an absence of a few years to Khartoum,
where he got an almost kingly welcome. The people,
remembering him as a wise and kind ruler, thronged
round him and bowed themselves to the sand
before him. Had he not always been the champion
of the slave ? They were glad that he had come to
protect them against the wild fanatical horde of
Egyptians who had chosen as their leader the Mahdi,
a man who supported the horrible practice of
slavery. But the confidence of the people began to
fail ; for their enemies swarmed round the city, and
instead of more soldiers being sent out from Britain
to help Gordon, he was told to do the best he could,
alone. It was hard enough to keep the enemy out,
but when treachery crept into the city itself his task
became a hopeless one, and he wrote the message :
" If the expeditionary force does not come in ten
days the town may fall, and I have done my best
for the honour of our country.—Goodbye. C. G.
GORDON."

But relief did not come in ten days—nor even in

forty ! On a January night in 1885 a traitor in the pay of the enemy stole through the streets of Khartoum and opened one of the gates to let the Mahdi's forces in. With wild yells of triumph they surged into that doomed city and nothing could be done to stop them. At the first alarm, General Gordon appeared at the door of his house and was about to descend into the courtyard below, when he was struck by the enemy's bullets, and fell dead. At daybreak not a living man was left to defend the British flag which had flown there for so long and was now hauled down. Two days afterwards the relief force arrived, but alas ! too late to save the town and the gallant soldier who had died in its defence. A new Khartoum has risen over the ruins left by the Mahdi's soldiers. Khartoum is a fine city, and one of its finest buildings is the Gordon Memorial College. But to all true Britons Gordon needs no memorial. His bravery and his patriotism will never die !

XIII

CLAN MACLEAN

THE CLAN MACLEAN—or Clan Gillian, to give it the older name—consisted of four separate branches. No one of these branches was overlord of the others, because they all held their lands from the Lord of the Isles. There were Macleans of Duart, Maclaines of Lochbuie, Macleans of Coll, and Macleans of Ardgour. Of the four the Macleans of Duart were the most influential. Their founder was called Lachlan; he became Steward of the Lord of the Isles, whose daughter he married.

The question, "Then who is Chief of *all* the Macleans?" would be rather difficult to answer.

Coll and Ardgour would probably not dispute the claims of Duart to that distinction, because they were, without doubt, branches of the Duart Clan. And although the Lochbuie family was also descended from Duart, their branch was from a Duart of a much earlier date and they refuse to acknowledge the claim of the Duart Chief to the chiefdom of *all* the Macleans !

It is a strange and rather sad thing that of all the great properties which once belonged to the two greater branches, only a few acres remain in their possession.

The origin of the Macleans is a matter of uncertainty. One opinion is that they are of Norman descent. But tradition gives it that the Clan was descended from a famous Celtic warrior who was known as " Gillian-na-Tuaigh " (" Gillian of the Battle-axe "). And certainly the Macleans use as their crest a battle-axe between laurel and cypress branches. There is, of course, a story connected with the crest. It is that Gillian was engaged in a stag-hunt on Ben Talaidh, a mountain in Mull, and that in the excitement of the chase he wandered away from the rest of the party. A thick mist came down and enveloped the mountain and he completely lost his way. He wandered about for three days without being able to regain the lost track or find his companions. Then, being utterly tired out, he crept under a laurel bush and after fixing the handle

A THICK MIST CAME DOWN AND ENVELOPED THE MOUNTAIN AND HE
LOST HIS WAY COMPLETELY

of the battle-axe in the earth, he lay down and slept the sleep of exhaustion. When evening came, his friends who had been seeking him saw the head of the axe above the bush and, when they looked underneath, there was Gillian sleeping on the ground with his arm round the handle ! It was said that at the Battle of Largs the same battle-axe did great execution among Haco's men.

The Macleans have royal Stewart blood in their veins, for a Maclean of Duart married a daughter of Alexander Stewart, Earl of Mar, who was grandson of Robert II. The grandson of this pair led Clan Maclean at Flodden and there he fell, it is said, in trying to save the life of James IV by placing his body between the King and the English arrows.

Another great family into which the Macleans married was that of the Earl of Argyll. The marriage of one of the Argylls (in the sixteenth century) was far from happy and, according to an old legend, her husband, Lachlan Maclean, made up his mind to get rid of his wife. No doubt there were faults on both sides. Rumour says that the lady had more than once tried to kill her husband ! Still, it was a pretty cold-blooded scheme of his to have her placed on a rock which was exposed only at low tide, and left there, with the horrible prospect of being sur-rounded and eventually drowned when the tide rose ! The rock, which is still known as the " Lady's

H

Rock," lies between the coast of Mull and the Island of Lismore, and has always been a danger to shipping. Luckily for Lady Elizabeth a boat happened to come that way and she was rescued from her terrible plight and taken to her brother's house. Her relations were naturally furious at the husband's conduct and, some time afterwards, when the Laird of Duart was in Edinburgh, a brother-in-law, Sir John Campbell, went to his lodging and finding the Laird in bed stabbed him with a dirk. So the insult to the proud family of Argyll was avenged !

Although the Macleans were related to the Macdonalds the two Clans were continually at variance. After bickerings which lasted for fully a century, proceedings came to a head between them in a violent battle over some lands in Islay. On the eve of this battle Sir Lachlan consulted a famous witch with regard to the prospects of his Clan in the battle which was before them. She warned him that, if he wished for success, on no account should he land on Islay on a Thursday ; and that he must not drink out of a spring there called " Strange Neil's Well." Luck was certainly against Lachlan for, a storm coming up on the Thursday, he was compelled to run for the nearest land, which, as it happened, was Islay ! And being very thirsty after landing, he drank deeply from a spring, not knowing that it was the very well which he had been warned against! People were very superstitious in those days and they believed that the disaster which followed was entirely due to his disregard of the witch's warning. But that was not all. Before the battle, a dwarf from Jura who was known as "Dubh Sith" (Black Elf) went to Sir Lachlan and offered to help him. Maclean disdained the assistance of such a little fellow and only laughed. The dwarf, full of rage at the contempt of the big man, went and offered himself to the leader on the other side, who promptly accepted his help. Of course no one expected "Dubh Sith" to fight on equal terms with the brawny Highlanders, but he had his own way of doing things. He was a nimble climber and he made for a high tree from which he could see the fighters. He saw Sir Lachlan climb a little knoll from which to overlook the course of the battle, and his sharp eyes noted an open joint in Sir Lachlan's armour. He fitted an arrow to his bowstring, carefully took aim, and the arrow finding the open joint ended Maclean's life! Both sides had great numbers killed and wounded in this fight, which is known as the battle of the Rhinns of Islay.

The Maclaines of Lochbuie were nearly as famous as the Duart family. They had great possessions which included part of the mainland and the islands of Tiree, Jura, Scarba and Mull. When one of the chiefs of Lochbuie died, his heir was only a baby, called Murdoch Gearr. Maclean of Duart, seeing his chance, invaded and seized the lands of the infant heir. He would have seized the child as well, but some kindly people managed to convey him secretly to Ireland. There he was cared for, and when he grew up he determined to try and regain his own estates. With a number of brave Irishmen he set sail for Mull. On his arrival, he was recognised by his old nurse, who knew him by a mole on his breast. She persuaded her husband who was doorkeeper of the Castle of Lochbuie to open the gate, and the young heir rushed in at the head of his supporters. Having in this way taken the occupants of the castle by surprise, he soon made himself its master. The two branches of the Clan fought a pitched battle near Grulin in which the Duart Macleans were defeated. When Lochbuie was returning home in triumph after the battle, he came across Duart with a party of men asleep on the ground. Lochbuie drew his dirk and cautiously twisted it in his rival's hair, sticking its point into the ground. When Maclean of Duart awoke and found his hair fastened to the ground, he recognised the dirk and the generosity of his rival in not killing him when he had the opportunity. He never afterwards interfered with Maclaine of Lochbuie and the two families were friends from that time onwards.

In Highland history there are a great many examples of the fidelity of clansmen to their Chief.

One of them is found in the origin of the Maclean slogan—or war-cry—" Another for Hector ! " In the Battle of Inverkeithing between Cromwell's troops and those of Charles II, a father and seven sons are known to have sacrificed themselves for their Chief, Sir Hector Maclean of Duart. In the fight the Macleans were surrounded by the English and were being cut to pieces. Seeing that the aim of the enemy was to kill or capture the Chief, the old man and his sons surrounded Sir Hector, and at every attempt on his life one of them thrust himself forward to take the fatal blow, crying, " Another for Hector ! " and the eight Macleans lay dead before Sir Hector fell. There is an old ballad about it which begins :

> " Sir Hector Roy, the stout Maclean,
> Fought, one to ten, but all in vain,
> His broad claymore unsheathing ;
> Himself lay dead 'mid heaps of slain
> For Charles at Inverkeithing."

When the Rebellion of 1715 broke out, the Chief, Sir John Maclean, fought with his Clan on the Stuart side. Then when it was known that Prince Charlie was coming, Sir Hector, the Chief in 1745, crossed over from France to Edinburgh with the intention of assisting. As part of his first equipment he wanted a good stout pair of brogues for campaigning, and, knowing that one of his clansmen in Edinburgh made good shoes, he went to him to place an order, asking him to keep the purpose for which they were intended secret. But the shoe-maker's wife was so proud of having the Chief in her home that she could not keep the secret! The authorities heard of it and they promptly arrested Sir Hector and kept him safe for two years! So he was not with the Clan at Culloden where they fought in the first line.

In our own times a Maclean had the unusual experience of being kidnapped by bandits and held to ransom. This happened in 1907 to Sir Harry Maclean (of Drimnin) whose Eastern title was " Kaid Maclean." He was instructor to the Moorish army, afterwards becoming colonel of the Sultan of Morocco's bodyguard. While on a mission from the Sultan he was captured by Mulai Ben Mohammed Raisuli, a Moroccan bandit, who had terrorised the whole district round Tangier with his outrages on Europeans and natives alike. To take captive a well-known Scotsman like Sir Harry Maclean was a piece of cool audacity. But, once captured, Raisuli steadily refused to let him go until the enormous sum of £20,000 was paid as ransom. And at the end of eight months the British Government had to pay it.

The present Chief of the Macleans, Colonel Sir Fitzroy Donald Maclean, is ninety-six years of age.

He served in the Crimean War, getting his commission from the great Duke of Wellington.[1] It is pleasant to think that the representative of this ancient family should have had twenty years' enjoyment of the home of his ancestors.

" Huile latha sona dhuibh gun latha idir dona dhuibh ! (May all his days be gladness with ne'er an hour of sadness.) "

Hundreds of years of Clan fighting naturally make a hardy race of soldiers and the Macleans have never been backward in military service. In 1775 a battalion commanded by Lieut.-Col. Alan Maclean of Torloisk was raised from Highlanders who had settled in Canada, and was used for active service there. In the Great War, Canada raised a battalion called the Maclean Highlanders. This battalion fought splendidly in France, and when the war was over they sent their banners to Duart Castle where they hang side by side with the colours of the old 84th Regiment in the hall of that ancient place, which is once more the natural centre of all descendants of the " Children of the Mist "—Clan Gillean.

[1] His boyhood's ambition to restore the ruined walls of his ancestral home was realised when Duart Castle came into his possession in the year 911, and the old home was re-established.

XIV

CLAN MACLEOD

TRADITION reports that Leod, the earliest ancestor of the Macleods, was a royal viking —no less a personage than the son of Olaf, the Black King of Man ! That is how the Macleods are entitled to use in their coat-of-arms the three legs which form the armorial bearings of the Isle of Man.

Leod married the heiress of Dunvegan who was the daughter of a Norwegian chief. They had two sons, Tormod, who founded the family of Macleod of Harris and Dunvegan ; and Torquil, whose race held the Lewis and Assynt.

One of the most interesting of Tormod's descendants was Rory Mor of Dunvegan, who raised himself from the position of an outlawed chief to one of honour in the Highlands. When James VI was King of Scotland, he found confusion about the ownership of land in the Highlands and Islands, and he ordered all chiefs to produce the charters to their estates. Both families of Macleod resisted the order : he therefore declared their land forfeit. A large number of people were brought from Fifeshire to settle on the Island of Lewis, but the Macleods saw to it that they had no peace in their new surroundings, and after a dangerous and uncomfortable time they went back to Fife. The experiment was tried three times without success, so in the end the King gave up the scheme. Rory Mor was able to get a free pardon and afterwards was given a knighthood by the King. Rory turned out a most successful ruler of his estates, doing his best to secure peace among his neighbours. He was the first of the family who could write. An earlier chief who had occasion to sign his name to a document had to have his hand guided like a child.

Dunvegan Castle, the family seat of Tormod's branch of the Macleods, built by Norsemen in the ninth or tenth century, is situated on precipitous rocks at the head of Loch Bracadale in the south-west of Skye. It is believed to be the oldest inhabited house in Scotland, and certainly is one of the most romantic. Many interesting relics are

treasured in the Castle. There is an ancient cup
or chalice of great beauty which Sir Walter Scott
wrote about in *The Lord of the Isles*. Then there is
the drinking-horn of Rory Mor, which is a great
ox-horn, tipped with silver. It holds two pints of
liquid and when a Macleod Chief comes of age, he is
expected to be able to drain its contents at one
draught !. The crest and motto of the Macleods
are a bull's head and the words " Hold fast ! "
The story which they commemorate is one told of a
Dunvegan chief who went to Inveraray to visit the
Earl of Argyll. He arrived upon a fateful day,
the day when, for some offence, one of the Campbell
clansmen had been condemned by Argyll to be gored
to death by a bull. A sort of arena had been prepared,
from the raised seats of which Argyll and his guests
could view the wretched man's death. At the hour
arranged, the bull, bellowing with rage, was brought
in and afterwards the man, who, whatever his feelings
were, showed no fear as he faced the powerful
animal. Macleod begged Argyll to pardon him.
" Impossible," said Argyll. " Nothing can save him
now ! "   " But," said Macleod, as he rose and threw
off his cloak, " if I save him will you give him to me ? "
" Oh yes," said Argyll, " if you save him he is yours,
but I warn you, you go to your death ! "   Quick
as thought Macleod sprang into the arena, rushed
to the bull, whose head was now lowered for the
fatal thrust, and seized one of the horns with his left

hand. As he did so the cry " Hold fast ! " rang
out from one of the spectators. And " hold fast "
he did ! The next moment he struck a blow with
his dirk which pierced its heart and the great animal
fell dead ! There are still Campbells at Dunvegan
who claim to be descended from the man whom
Macleod saved.

Perhaps the most curious of the many relics at
Dunvegan is the Brattich Shithe, or consecrated
banner of the Clan, commonly called the Fairy Flag.
It is like a pennon and is made of silk, with what
look rather like berries of reddish colour, worked or
sewed on the silk. There are two legends relating
how it came into the possession of the Macleods.
One tells that a fairy princess whom a Macleod
married was called back to fairyland, and that as
she fled she dropped her cloak. It is said that the
Fairy Flag is the cloak the princess left behind !
And the other story is that once upon a time an
heir having been born to one of the chiefs, there
were of course great rejoicings at Dunvegan. While
the infant slept, his nurse stole away to look on at
the gay doings, and in her absence the bedclothes
slipped off the babe. Then fairies, who were watching over him, wrapped him in the silken flag, and
when the nurse returned and found the strange
covering upon the child she carried the babe,
wrapped as he was, into the great hall. As she
entered there came the sound of fairy voices which

told that the flag they had used had magic powers ; that, if produced in battle, it would make an enemy see many times the number of Macleods who were actually there ; that it would ensure the succession of the family ; and that it would bring herring (which meant prosperity) into the Loch. But it must be used only three times, for, if waved on a fourth occasion, the flag and its bearer would disappear from earthly ken. It is said that it has been used twice with results exactly as promised by the fairies !

The Macleods, like the Macleans, were continually at variance with the Clan Macdonald. Three weeks after a very hot fight—in which the Macleods had the worst of it—Rory Mor Macleod was giving a feast to some of his clansmen in Harris. That night there was a great storm and after one tremendous gust of wind Rory exclaimed, " What a night is this ! If my greatest enemy were to ask shelter from me to-night, I would not refuse it ! " He was very much taken aback when he was told that some of the Macdonalds (who were on their way to Skye) had been caught in the storm and had run for Harris ; and that, even then, " Donald Mac Ian 'Ic Sheumais " was at his door ! Rory would not go back on his word, so the Macdonalds were invited to come in and sit down to supper. All was going well when one of them made an indiscreet remark about the recent fight. Instantly

every Macleod sprang to his feet, weapon in hand,—
but a shout from the Macleod Chief rang out above
the storm, ordering his clansmen to sit down and
not disgrace his hospitality! The Macdonalds
were given sleeping-quarters in a house nearby,
but before they left the castle a young servant
gave them a significant hint that " the wind was now
fair for Skye ! " Acting on it they quietly returned
to their ship and set sail. Well for them that they
did so, for one Macleod must have forgotten the
honour of his Chief, and from the sea they saw great
flames rising from the very house in which they were
supposed to be sleeping !

In comparison with the Macleods of Dunvegan
and Harris, the Macleods of Lewis and Assynt had a
very chequered career. Their race began with a
Torquil and ended with a Torquil. In the end of
the sixteenth century their branch of the Clan was
extinguished by the Mackenzies of Kintail who were
also connections by marriage. The story of their
extinction is one of the most painful chapters in
Highland history, for it is one long record of murder
and treachery. Mackenzie was aided and abetted
by some Macleods who bore a grudge to Black
Torquil, the last Chief—and one must allow that
Torquil had in various ways earned the dislike of
his neighbours. Whether or not, he was invited to
bring his followers to a banquet on board a wine-
carrying Dutch vessel which had been captured off

Raasay. Scarcely had the guests seated themselves when they were all seized, tied with cords and carried off to Kintail in West Ross, where Mackenzie ordered that they should be beheaded. At the hour fixed for the execution there came a violent earthquake which terrified everybody—including the executioners. But it did not hinder them from committing the terrible deed ; in fact it is said that they hurried to get it over ! Mackenzie in this way came into possession of Lewis and Assynt. The chiefdom passed to the Macleods of Raasay, and, when their line failed, it went to Macleod of Cadboll in Easter Ross.

A Macleod chief at one time married the widow of a Mathieson, chief of Lochalsh. The union so much displeased her young sons that one of them went to his grandfather, the Mackintosh, and asked for assistance to turn Macleod out of the Castle of Lochalsh. He returned with a following and attacked the castle, which Macleod and his wife defended. At last the attackers set fire to the building and then young Mathieson took up position at the gate, so as to allow his mother—but not his stepfather—to pass out. When she went he was relieved to know that she was safe, but you can imagine his anger when he found that, in the confusion, Macleod had passed out along with her, sheltered under her big plaid !

Two events occurred in those olden days which must bring regret to all Macleods. After the great

HE GAVE HIMSELF UP TO MACLEOD OF ASSYNT

Duke of Montrose was defeated at Carbisdale in
Ross-shire, he wandered westwards, his only food
for four days being a little bread and milk from a
poor cottar's wife ; and he gave himself up to
Macleod of Assynt, from whom he had reason to
expect assistance. Instead of getting help, he found
himself a prisoner, and Macleod handed him over
to the Covenanters. From Assynt he was taken to
Edinburgh and executed. The darkest blot on the
Macleods is the Eigg Massacre in 1577, when the
whole population of the Island of Eigg was suffocated
in a cave.

But it is unnecessary to dwell on these terrible
times, now long past, when violence and bloodshed
were rather the rule than the exception in the western
Highlands and Islands. At the time of the Jacobite
Rising of 1745 the Macleods were divided in their
sympathies. The Macleods of Raasay were all for
Prince Charlie, but the Chief took the other side.
All the same, carefully kept among the treasures at
Dunvegan are various relics of Prince Charlie and
Flora Macdonald. Indeed, one of the Prince's most
devoted companions during his wanderings in the
islands after his defeat at Culloden was a Macleod.

From some information given by " the Chevalier
de Macleot " at Lisle in 1787, there would seem to
have been a considerable branch of the Clan settled
in France since 1530, descended from David MacLeod,
Gendarme of the Scottish Guard. " The present

I

head of the family (1794) is Jean Nicolas de Macleot, Seigneur de Terreigne Pierreville, before the Revolution, gentilhomme ordinair du Roi."

In modern times the most famous member of the Clan was the great divine, Dr. Norman Macleod. He belonged to the Morven branch and had a distinguished career as a minister of the Church of Scotland and as a writer. He became chaplain to Queen Victoria and for many years was her trusted friend. He is spoken of by Scottish people, all the world over, as " the great Dr. Norman Macleod."

And just a word about the MacCrimmons, that most famous family of Scottish pipers. They are a sept of the Macleods, and for centuries they have been hereditary pipers to the chiefs of the Clan. Their piping was so wonderful that the Skye people said they owed their art to fairy help ! After the last Jacobite Rising an Act of Parliament abolished among other things the retaining of pipers by the chiefs, and the greatness of the MacCrimmons waned, as one by one they disappeared. The last of the MacCrimmons prepared to go to Canada and, before going, it is said he composed the famous lament called *Ha til, ha til, ha til, MacCrimmon !* (" No more, no more, no more, MacCrimmon ! ") He reached Greenock, but he never embarked, for the love of Skye drew him home again to his beloved island, and there he lived until his death in 1822 at ninety-one years of age.

XV

CLAN ROSS—OR CLAN ANRIAS

THE origin of Ross as a Clan name is easy to understand. It is taken from the name of the County of Ross. But the alternative name, Clan Anrias, admits of more than one explanation. The best known is that a member of the Clan in olden days was a monk or abbot devoted to the service of St. Andrew, the Patron Saint of Scotland ; there is another which will be told in due course. It is contained in a curious sixteenth-century manuscript which was found among other old documents at Balnagown Castle, the family seat of the Rosses. It is called " Ane breve Cronicle of the Erlls of Ross " and it begins by telling how the first earl got his title. The historian who deciphered the manuscript said that the dates in the story are by no means historically accurate. But seven hundred years separate from our own day the particular incident about which he was doubtful, so most people will be content to accept it as it stands! The story is related as follows. When Edward I became King of England there was a great concourse of people from all parts of the country to see the Coronation festivities in London, and representatives of all the great Scottish families were invited to attend, because Margaret, the Scottish Queen, was the sister of the new King. At that time there was at the English Court a famous French wrestler from Normandy. This wrestler was marvellously strong and so skilful in the art that, although he had been challenged over and over again, no one had been able to overthrow him. But during the gay doings at the Coronation he was challenged by Farquhar Ross, a vassal of King Alexander, from the far north of Scotland, and to the amazement of the Court and the delight of the Scottish King, Farquhar overthrew and finally vanquished the great fighter! King Alexander was so pleased with Farquhar's " notabill vassalage "—as he called it—that he gave him the Earldom of Ross. Farquhar gave the credit of his victory to a vow that he had made that, if he should be victorious in the fight, he would found an abbey of the first religious Order whose members he should happen to meet in Scotland. On his way to the north he came across two "white canons" (or monks) from Whithorn Abbey in Galloway, and he took them home with him to Ross-shire. He founded an abbey of this Order at Fearn near Kincardine in Ross, which later fell into disrepair, so another abbey was built at Fearn in Easter Ross, which is in use to-day as a Parish Church.

From Farquhar five Earls of Ross descended, all of whom made marriages of importance. One of them married the sister of Robert the Bruce—who was a personal friend and for whom he fought at Bannockburn. And the daughter of Earl Hugh became the second wife of Robert II of Scotland. At that time Scotland and England were at war and Earl Hugh was killed in the defeat of the Scots at Halidon Hill near Berwick, where the English forces carried all before them. After that, the storm centre of all the fighting between the two nations was the City of Perth, which is the gate of the Highlands, as well as an important vantage point of mid Scotland. The people of Perth must have had a most uncomfortable time in those days for the city was held sometimes by the Scots and sometimes by the English. During the last time that the English held the city they spent vast sums in fortifying it, so that to the Scots besiegers it seemed impregnable. Even when French ships of war sailed up the River Tay, the moat which surrounded the town pre-

vented the placing of the Scots engines of war within
firing distance. The Earl of Ross hit at length upon
the solution of the difficulty. He brought a large
body of miners upon the scene and directed them
to excavate underground ; in this way all the water
from the moat was drained away. The engines of
war could then be brought up and placed against
the walls of the city. Even the heavens helped the
Scots, for on the day fixed for the attack there was an
eclipse of the sun which terrified the garrison. And
although the besieging army also felt far from
comfortable about such an unusual phenomenon,
they realised the advantage which the growing
darkness gave them and took the chance to place
their pieces in readiness. When the eclipse passed,
the English Governor saw the strong position of
the Scots and he came to terms and gave up the
town.

Earl William, the hero of Perth, had two daughters,
but no heir. The younger daughter married Donald,
Lord of the Isles, and Euphemia was heiress to her
father. She was courted by Walter Lesley from
Aberdeenshire who is called in the " Breve Cronicle "
a " nobill valzeant man." She liked the noble valiant
Lesley very much, but she liked the name of Ross
still better, and she refused to marry him unless
he would take *her* name. He agreed and became
Walter Ross, and their son was Alexander, Earl of
Ross. The line of the ancient earls ended with

Alexander's daughter, who became a nun and resigned her claim to the earldom in favour of her uncle, the Earl of Buchan.

Then Donald, Lord of the Isles, claimed the earldom for his wife, who was also a Ross. Donald gathered a great army and marched into Ross-shire, sweeping all before him. His success so emboldened him that he took his army right across Scotland, carrying destruction in his path. In Aberdeenshire the Earl of Mar had assembled an army to meet the marauders and a great battle took place at Harlaw near Inverurie. All day long the battle raged, with dreadful slaughter on both sides, and with the advantage to the Lord of the Isles. Darkness fell, and Mar and the survivors had to pass the night on the field of battle in full expectation that with morning light there would be renewed attack. When day dawned it was found that the Lord of the Isles had retreated and was well on his way westwards ! And although there were new hostilities later he was compelled to resign his claim to the Earldom of Ross and become instead a vassal to the Scottish Crown. This battle left its result on the music and folk history of the country. For many years a march called *The Battle of Harlaw* was very popular throughout Scotland ; and so was a ballad which describes the meeting of the armies and the progress of the battle—and what happened after :

" Then Donald fled and that full fast,
    To mountains hich for all his micht,
For he and his were all agast,
    And ran till they were out of sicht.
And sua [so] of Ross he lost his richt,
    Thoch mony men with him he brocht
Towards the Yles fled day and nicht,
    And all he wan was deirlie bocht."

The Lairds of Balnagown were descended from Hugh, Earl of Ross, who was killed at Halidon Hill. (His second son, Hugh, was Laird of Balnagown and Rarichie.) The fifth Laird in this line married Katharine McLendris, daughter of Paul MacTyre McLendris, and in the " Breve Cronicle " we read " after whilk marriage *Ross are called Clan Lendris* " : so that is the second explanation of the name " Clan Anrias."

There is a funny old legend at the end of the " Breve Cronicle " of the " Erlls of Ross " which links the origin of Paul MacTyre with that of the Macleods. According to the legend : There were three sons of the King of Denmark who came over the sea and landed in the northern parts of Scotland to conquer by the sword and gain lands for themselves. Ewine conquered Caithness ; Loid (or Leod) conquered the lands of the Lewis, and Lendries conquered a part of Sutherland and that part of Ross which belonged to the Earls of Ross. Paul MacTyre

was the grandson of that Lendris. He was powerful
and ruthless, and in his day was a sort of Northern
Rob Roy. The manuscript calls him " ane takand
man "—which is another way of saying that he
helped himself ! Cattle were the form of blackmail
which he mainly extorted from weaker people, and
it was reported that every year, as long as he was
fit to travel, he took nine score of cattle out of
Caithness alone ! When he became infirm his son
went in his stead to take toil of the Caithness cattle.
But while the Caithness folks were in dread of Paul
and never dared to resist him, they had no feeling
of that sort for Murthro Reoch, his son, for they
banded themselves together and lay in wait for him
and killed him. When the news reached the father
the manuscript tells that he " deyit for displeasor
of his sone." Later the friends of the family sent
for the bones of the dead Murthro that they might
be laid in his father's grave, and there is a queer
old rhyme which tells what happened :

" This Murthro Reoch of whome ye now do reid
    Throw tyrannie was slaine as ye heir tell.
The eldest sone of Paul MacTyre indeed
    Was buryed in Caithness quhair the caise befell.
Quhen freindis tharafter taik yame to counsell
    And send in haist ane young man for his baines
Quha coming home with them in Helmisdaill
    Drownit thairin he and they all at aines."

The messenger apparently tried to cross the Moray Firth from Helmsdale and met with disaster. Seafaring people consider that a dead body in a boat always brings ill-luck, and no doubt the misfortune was looked upon as a judgment.

The Balnagown line of Rosses failed when David, the thirteenth Laird, had no heir, and the estate was conveyed to the Rosses of Hawkhead, an old family of great repute, but in no way related to the family of the ancient earls. And, rather curiously, in the fifteenth century a member of this Ross family was chosen to be one of the Scottish champions to fight with three knights of Burgundy in the presence of James II ; and for the second time in their history a Ross defeated a Frenchman in a king's Court !

The Rosses have made their mark in many spheres of life. Just a hundred years ago, a contribution to the knowledge of the polar regions, which sent a wave of interest through the scientific world, was made by Rear-Admiral Sir John Ross and his nephew, Rear-Admiral Sir James Clark Ross. They discovered the magnetic North Pole, and after planting the British flag there they returned home with a collection of valuable scientific data. This stood Sir James Clark Ross in good stead when he was appointed to command an expedition to the Antarctic, during which he discovered a mountainous land which he named Victoria Land, and a smoking volcano, which he named after his ship, Mount Erebus. In memory of this explorer, the sea which bounds that rocky coastline was called the Ross Sea. And so, in that far southern land, there will live for ever a name which brings to Scottish minds not only the brave man for whose sake it was given, but also thoughts of that beautiful romantic county in the far north of Scotland which is the cradle of the great Ross Clan.

XVI

CLAN FRASER

THE original name of the Frasers was Frizel or Frasele, and it is generally agreed that they were of Norman origin. The name is said to be derived from the French word " fraise "—meaning " strawberry." According to the story an ancestor called Julius de Berry of Bourbon entertained one of the Kings of France to a dish of very large, luscious strawberries, which he had grown in his garden. (Cream is not mentioned, by the way !) But it is said that the King enjoyed the fruit so much that he gave de Berry a knighthood and allowed him to use the strawberry leaf in his coat-of-arms ; and that the name of the family was changed at that time to "Fraisele" or "Fraiseur."

The Frasers have the strawberry leaves on their shield, along with three crowns, which were added after the marriage of one of them to a niece of King Robert I. Their motto is French—*Je suis prest*—(I am ready).

It is stated that Frasers appeared in the south of Scotland early in the twelfth century and began to acquire land. In those days there were two ways in which Norman adventurers became permanent settlers in Scotland. One was by force of the sword and the other by marriage with an heiress of the country. And sometimes land was granted to them by reigning monarchs who had French blood in their veins.

The Frasers gained their first hold by a judicious marriage with the heiress of Tweeddale. By degrees they made their way northwards, eventually establishing themselves in Aberdeenshire and Inverness-shire. In Aberdeenshire they settled at Philorth in the north-east corner of the county, and one of them in 1537 founded the town of Fraserburgh. He even established a university in the town, but it did not last very long. The ninth of the Frasers of Philorth raised a regiment for the King's service at the Battle of Worcester and, on the death of his cousin, he inherited the Earldom of Saltoun, which still belongs to the family.

Of the Inverness-shire branch, one member was killed at the Battle of Halidon Hill in 1333. His son was the first to be entitled " of Lovat." From that time onwards the Frasers played an important part in the Clan life of the Highlands. Castle Dounie, their early stronghold, was burned down after the " 'Forty-five," and its successor, Beaufort Castle, was built a little distance from the old site. It is an ideally situated castle, and the whole of the Fraser country is marvellously beautiful and varied. Its wild inaccessible straths were of particular value in the old days of Clan warfare. It has many lochs and fine rivers with valuable salmon fisheries. In late summer the salmon make their way up the rivers to their breeding-places in mountain lochs, and the gleaming fish, leaping up the falls at various points on the rivers, are a wonderful sight. There is a particular rock on the edge of one of the Beauly falls which the salmon make a half-way stage. One Lord Lovat, it is said, once placed a faggot fire and a kettle of water on this rock. It had not been there long when a salmon leapt right into the pot and in a very short time it was ready for the table ! After that Lord Lovat was able to tell neighbours who boasted of their salmon-fishings that *he* had a salmon leap where the fish, when wanted, jumped into the pot and were boiled then and there !

The early days of Clan Fraser were full of quarrels with neighbouring Clans. One of these led to a

pitched battle between the Frasers and Clanranald.
A young Clanranald had been brought up at Castle
Dounie and, when he rather unexpectedly became
Chief of the Clanranald, he was practically unknown
to his own people. Great preparations had been
made to give him a handsome reception, but he
apparently looked upon all the fuss as unnecessary
and extravagant, and even told his clansmen it was
a pity to have slaughtered so many cattle and sheep—
" A few hens would have done as well ! " To the
Clan the remark showed a small mean mind and they
promptly let him know that a " hen chief " was no
chief for them, and practically drove him out.
" Ranald of the Hens," as they called him, went
straight back to the Frasers and roused them to
help him. The two Clans met at Loch Lochy side
on a hot July day and, from the circumstances of the
Frasers having thrown off all garments except their
kilts and shirts, that battle has ever since been known
as " Blar na Leine " (" The Field of Shirts ").
The slaughter was dreadful, and out of many hundreds only ten were left alive on each side.

A Lovat chief also was once given the cold
shoulder by some of his clansmen—just after the
revolution which dethroned James VII. After
William of Orange had come to the throne of
Britain at the invitation of the English and a section
of the Scottish people, Lord Tullibardine, the son
of the Marquis of Atholl, raised a body of Atholl

Highlanders, which included three hundred Frasers, and placed them under the command of Hugh, Lord Lovat. The men were practically all Jacobites, and they thought they had been recruited to help the abdicated Stewart King. When they were addressed by their leaders at Blair Castle and told that they had been raised to support King William, they felt that they had been betrayed. Without hesitation they rushed from their ranks to the nearest burn, where they filled their bonnets with water and drank to the health of " King James ! " Then putting Stewart of Ballechin at their head, they marched away with pipes playing and colours flying to " follow the bonnets of Bonnie Dundee." His heroic exploits had stirred their admiration and they were glad and proud to fight under him. But their jubilation over the result of the Battle of Killie-crankie was turned into mourning when it became known that their gallant leader had been killed almost at the moment of victory.

One of the most extraordinary characters in Highland history was a Fraser—Simon, twelfth Lord Lovat, whose Clan title was Mac Shimi (Son of Simon). He was a Jacobite intriguer who was not above professing loyalty to King William for the purpose of betraying him. Twice he was out-lawed (once for high treason) and he fled to France, where he joined the exiled Stewart King. When he ventured back to Britain he was arrested in

London. But when he called his Clan out on the Government side at the Rebellion of the " 'Fifteen," King William granted him a full pardon, and he was made Sheriff of Inverness. He commanded one of the newly formed companies of the Black Watch, and, given a favourable chance, he would have used his Company against the King without any compunction. He was a master of the rather risky art of " sitting on the fence "—with his weight now on one side and now on the other—although his inclinations were really for the Stewarts. The promise of a dukedom led him to join in an invitation to Prince Charles Edward to invade Scotland and secure the throne for his father, yet, when the Rebellion of the " 'Forty-five " actually began, it found Lord Lovat professing loyalty to the other side! But this time he had over-reached himself. His double-dealing had been proved beyond doubt and, after the Battle of Culloden, flight was his only course. He met Prince Charlie then for the first and only time and, when the Prince told him that the cause was lost, Simon rated him soundly, telling him that his great ancestor, Robert the Bruce, had lost eleven battles, but had won Scotland by the twelfth! That night Lovat was carried to Glenstrath-farrar and, from a hilltop on his way to that inaccessible spot, he saw one of the first acts of Cumberland's soldiers—his own Castle Dounie, the centre of his ambitions, blazing and lighting up the darkness

K

for miles around. Simon was now an old man and he could not walk a step unsupported, so for his movement from one hiding-place to another he was entirely dependent on the help and devotion of his clansmen. They must have carried him about seventy miles from Glenstrath-farrar to the hiding-place which he had carefully prepared on an island on Loch Morar. There was only one boat on the loch and that was in his possession, but his enemies were too ingenious for him. Word had got about that Simon was hiding somewhere about the loch, which only a narrow peninsula separates from the sea. So some men from a man-of-war which was lying off-shore towed a boat over the narrow neck of land and launched it on Loch Morar! After that Simon's capture was only a matter of time, and he was discovered—so it is said—hiding in the trunk of a hollow tree into which he had crept. One of the seamen was astonished to see, in an opening in the tree trunk, two human legs, all encased in flannel—and he knew that the chase was at an end! The old Chief was carried in a litter to London, and there he was tried and executed in 1747.

While Lord Lovat was in exile in France, one of his kinsmen—Major James Fraser of Castle Leather —was selected by the Clan to carry a message to him. The Major's knowledge of the French language consisted of just three words, yet he made his way from Calais to Paris and then to Saumur, where

THE CENTRE OF HIS AMBITIONS LIGHTING UP THE DARKNESS FOR MILES
AROUND

Lovat was, without any trouble ! And he afterwards, at Lunéville, visited the exiled Stewart King, who was keen to know how the Major had managed. " Do you know no French at all ? " he asked. " Oh yes, Sire," said the Major, " I know three words—the first to ask the way, the second to ask for a bottle of wine, and the third a bed at night." James asked him to repeat the words, and the Major's Highland pride was much hurt at the laughter which followed his queer pronunciation. He drew himself up and said he was glad to have come so far to amuse his Majesty ! The Duke of Lorraine treated him as a sort of curiosity. " You actually walked all the way ? " the Duke asked. " Then I suppose you know nothing about horses ? " " I preferred to walk," the Major answered stiffly, " but, if you will try me with a horse, I'll show you whether I can ride or not." After dinner a hunt was got up and a bucking horse was given him to try his skill in riding. The Major not only kept his seat, but he outstripped the harriers and killed the hare with his whip before the hunt had properly begun ! He took every hedge and ditch that came in his way, and, although he lost his hat and his wig, he gave such entertainment to the ladies of the Court that they said it would be long before they would forget the " galloping Major ! "

Simon Fraser, the sixteenth and present Lord Lovat, raised and commanded a corps called the

Lovat Scouts in the early days of the Boer War. These northern Highlanders made splendid soldiers. A great many of them were gillies and stalkers, accustomed to game hunting and to rough hill and track riding, such as the regular troops found very trying on the veldt. Lord Lovat was mentioned in despatches, and the Scouts were specially commended by both Lord Roberts and Lord Kitchener. On his return from South Africa Lord Lovat raised a Yeomanry Regiment to form part of a Highland Mounted Brigade, of which he became Lieutenant-Colonel. When the Great War broke out, he commanded his Brigade at the front. In war, his name has been an incentive to patriotism, and in peace his relations with his Clan have always been an example of the true spirit of Highland fellowship.

XVII

CLAN STEWART

PRACTICALLY every branch of the Stewart family has in some part of its coat-of-arms a device which looks like a slice of a chessboard. Sir Walter Scott speaks of it as " The Stewart Chequer," but it is a recognised heraldic device which is known as the " Checky." Like other heraldic devices it has its history.

In olden times methods of reckoning accounts were very crude. No doubt the earliest accounts were kept by notches made on pieces of wood !

At the beginning of the twelfth century accounting was done in squares like those on a chess-board, which were ruled on a board or cloth round which the accountants or stewards sat. Calculations were made on the squares by means of counters which represented sums of money paid to or due by the Treasurer of Revenues.

It is amusing to read that minstrels were kept in attendance to discourse soothing music to the stewards during their complicated tasks !

The High Stewardship of Scotland was made a hereditary appointment in the family of Walter Fitz Alan, whose son introduced the device into the family coat-of-arms. It appeared on his seal, which was appended to the Charter of Melrose Abbey in the twelfth century.

Old names die hard. The Department of National Finance is still called " The Exchequer," and is a reminder of a method of reckoning which is now over seven hundred years old. The origin of the Stewarts is generally considered to be Norman, but in *The Story of the Stewarts* (which was printed for the Stewart Society) the descent of the Clan is traced from Banquo, Thane of Lochaber, and, through him, from the ancient Kings of Scotland.

When Banquo was murdered by Macbeth, King of Scotland, his son, Fleance, escaped and fled to the Court of Llewellen ap Griffith, Prince of Wales. Princess Nesta of Wales fell in love with him, and this made the noble lords about the Welsh Court so jealous that they eventually murdered him. His son, Walter, next incurred their ill-will, and when he grew up he had to seek safety in foreign lands. He attached himself to the Court of Alan the Red, of Brittany, whose daughter he married, and, out of compliment to his protector, took the name Fitz Alan (" Fitz " in the Welsh language meaning " son of " as " Mac " does in Scots).

When the Norman barons joined William the Conqueror in the invasion of England Walter accompanied his father-in-law, afterwards making his way to Scotland, the home of his ancestors. He was received with great favour by King David I of Scotland, who made him his High Steward. From that time onwards the Stewardship of Scotland remained in the family and—surnames having come into use about this period—the third hereditary High Steward settled the surname of Stewart on his descendants, among whom were the Earls of Monteith, Strathearn and Airth.

Alexander, the fourth Stewart, left two sons. Of these Sir James became the ancestor of the Royal Stewarts ; and Sir John became the ancestor of a number of Stewart families who were known as the Bonkyl branch. He had seven stalwart sons, each of whom founded a noble family in Scotland.

Among their descendants were the Earls of Angus, Lennox, Atholl, Buchan, Traquair, and Galloway ; the Lords of Lorn and Invermeath, Blantyre, Blessington, and Mountjoy ; the Stewarts of Appin and several other branches—a goodly array !

The sixth High Stewart (named Walter) being a great friend and supporter of Robert the Bruce, was given Bruce's daughter, Marjorie, for his wife. Robert II was the son of this marriage. He founded the line of Royal Stewarts, which for centuries drew the devotion and attachment of the Scottish people in such extraordinary measure.

It may be interesting to relate that Jean, the tenth child of King Robert II, was the direct ancestress of our two little Royal Princesses—Princess Elizabeth and Princess Margaret Rose, through their mother, Queen Elizabeth, who was the Lady Elizabeth Bowes-Lyon, daughter of the Earl of Strathmore. King Robert's daughter married Sir John Lyon, and when Sir John was killed in a private quarrel by Lord Lindsay of Crawford, King Robert took his young grandson, Lord Glamis, and had him brought up and educated at Court.

From this John, Lord Glamis, descend in a direct line the Earls of Strathmore and Kinghorn.

So many of the great Scottish families were related to the ruling family, that each king had to keep a watchful eye on his nobles, in case of plots to overthrow him. In the reign of Robert III one of the worst disturbers of the peace was the King's own brother, Alexander Stewart, Earl of Buchan, who was known as the Wolf of Badenoch. His stronghold was a castle on an island in Loch-an-Eilan in Invernessshire. The Wolf's lawlessness was notorious. Among other evil deeds he desecrated and burned down the beautiful cathedral of Elgin. The King was not strong enough to deal with him, and he continued to terrorise the northern half of the kingdom.

King Robert's other brother was also a menace to him. He was the Duke of Albany, Guardian of the Kingdom. Albany seized and imprisoned the King's elder son in Falkland Palace where it was said he died of starvation. In order to ensure the safety of his younger son, Prince James, King Robert sent him off to France to be educated, but the vessel in which he sailed was captured by an English ship and the boy was taken to London. There Henry IV imprisoned him in the Tower of London, and it was eighteen years before James was allowed to return to Scotland. The English extracted the sum of £40,000 before they would let him go, claiming this amount for having kept and educated him. In the interval King Robert had died, grief stricken at the capture of his boy, and James went back to Scotland as king. James I was outstanding among the Stewarts, because, in addition to being a splendid athlete and sportsman, he was very well educated, and he was also a poet and musician.

During his imprisonment in the Tower he wrote a long poem called *The King's Quair* in which he told how, day after day, he had seen a beautiful girl walking in the courtyard below his prison window. In the poem he called her his " milk-white dove."

She was the Lady Joan Beaufort, the daughter of the Duke of Somerset. He fell deeply in love with her, and after his freedom he took her back to Scotland with him as his Queen.

James I was assassinated at Perth in 1437.

Queen Joanna evidently favoured the Stewart Clan, because she afterwards married another Stewart husband—the Lord of Lorn.

The sons of her second marriage were ennobled by their step-brother James II. These he created respectively Earl of Buchan and Earl of Atholl. The Royal Stewarts were certainly an ill-fated race. Out of four kings named James not one di d a natural death. The fifth James, after losing two children, heard on his death-bed of the birth of a daughter to him. He had hoped for a son, and he sadly said, " It cam' wi' a lass and it will gang wi' a lass," meaning that the Crown of Scotland had come to the Stewarts by Marjorie Bruce, daughter of Robert I, and that it would be lost to them by the girl now born, afterwards Mary Queen of Scots.

Poor Mary ! she was misguided, passionate and wayward, but for all that, had the power to charm even those who disapproved of her, and retained that power to the day on which she was beheaded.

Every Royal Stewart had that power, but she had it in an unusual degree, and so had her descendant,

PRINCE JAMES A PRISONER IN THE TOWER OF LONDON

Bonnie Prince Charlie. Prince Charlie drew all hearts to him, and it is no exaggeration to say that people willingly died for him and for the cause which he represented.

One Stewart came very near to dying for Prince Charlie on account of his extraordinary likeness to the Prince.

We have seen that James II created one of his step-brothers Earl of Atholl. Nearly three hundred years later, a descendant of the Atholl family was so like Prince Charlie (James's descendant) that some time after the Battle of Culloden this Stewart was taken prisoner while working on his farm in Atholl.

The man who captured him was in great joy at having—as he thought—caught the Prince at last, and he saw himself in anticipation the possessor of the £30,000 which had been set upon Charles's head !

Young Stewart was taken to the Duke of Cumberland, and he owed his subsequent release entirely to his skill as a piper. It happened that an officer in Cumberland's army knew the tunes which Stewart played, and realised that only an Atholl man would be likely to know them. And, as he said, in no case could Prince Charlie be a proficient piper—so Stewart was allowed to go back to Atholl.

Although the word Clan is used for the Stewarts in general, the Appin branch was the only one which was governed entirely in the old Clan way and which followed a hereditary chief. When the male succession of the Lord of Lorn failed, a Stewart of Appin (who had married a Macdougal) got the lordship of Lorn.

The Campbells were near neighbours of Lorn and Appin, and at one time they seized the lands of Lorn and held them for several years. So it is not surprising that in spite of several intermarriages there should be frequent quarrels between the two Clans.

The Stewarts had many strongholds in Perthshire. Doune Castle was one of them. At one time it belonged to the Duke of Albany, brother of Robert III.

Then came the Stewarts of Methven and later the Stuarts of Lennox. One of these latter was created Lord Doune, and his son became Earl of Moray—the " Bonnie Earl of Moray " of the old song.

This Earl of Moray was very handsome, and the Queen looked on him with such favour that the King became jealous.

The Earl of Huntly was commissioned by King James to arrest Moray on a false charge and bring him into the royal presence. Moray escaped from his Castle of Donibristle in Fife, but was pursued and killed by Huntly. It is said that Huntly, who hated him, spitefully stabbed Moray's face. Moray with his last breath said, " You have spoilt a better face than your own ! "

The words of the ballad are :

" Ye Highlands and ye Lawlands,
      Oh ! where hae ye been ?
They hae slain the Earl of Moray
      And hae laid him on the green.

Now wae be to thee, Huntly,
      And wherefore did you sae ?
I bade you bring him wi' you
      But forbade you him to slay.

He was a braw gallant
      And he rade at the ring ;
And the bonny Earl of Moray
      Oh ! he might ha'e been a King !

He was a braw gallant
      And he played at the ba' ;
And the bonnie Earl of Moray
      Was the flow'r among them a'.

He was a braw gallant
      And he played at the glove ;
And the bonnie Earl of Moray
      Oh ! he was the Queen's love !

Oh ! lang will his lady
      Look owre the Castle Doune
Ere she see the Earl of Moray
      Come soundin' thro' the toun."

L

Other Stewart lines still surviving in Scotland are those of the Marquis of Bute ; the Stewarts of Ardvorlich, of Ballechin, of Garth, Strathdon, Strathspey, etc. The Dukes of Buccleuch, Lennox and Gordon, Grafton, and St. Albans are descended from Charles II ; and the Duke of Berwick and Alva (Spain), and Fitz James (France) from James II.

XVIII

CLAN MACLAREN OR MACLAURIN

ROMANCE tells us that the Clan MacLaren has a mermaid for one of its far back ancestors! She lived by the shores of the Island of Tiree, which belonged to a branch (or it may have been the main stem) of the Clan, and one impressionable young Chief fell in love with her and made her his wife— so the legends say.

Whether " they lived happy ever after," or whether, like the seal woman of the folk song, she was drawn to return periodically to her own home under the waves, we are not told. The only record of her connection with the family, outside of the legend, is to be found in her appearance in the

armorial bearings of the Clan, which were given by
the Lyon Court to Lord Dreghorn, a MacLaurin
who laid claim to the chiefship of the Clan in the
eighteenth century.

It is also claimed that the name " Laurin " comes
from St. Laurence, who was martyred in the time
of the Emperor Valerian when the Romans occupied
Britain.   So whether the MacLarens accept the
ancestry of the saint and martyr or that of the mermaid (or perhaps both) they have the satisfaction of
knowing that their origin is rather unique !

The MacLarens are certainly one of the original
Clans of Scotland.   In the days of Kenneth Alpin—
King of Scotland, they were granted lands in Bal-
quhidder and Strathearn, which have for many
centuries been known as the " Country of the Mac-
Larens."

Strathearn and Loch Earnside was at one time
regarded as holy ground, for it was there St. Fillan
lived and worked.   He sent his apostles as far afield
as Loch Tay, Glendochart and Breadalbane.   He
founded chapels, one at Killin, another at Strathfillan, and a third at Dundurn by Loch Earn.   When
he died at Dundurn and his congregation on Loch
Earn side would have liked to bury him there, the
people of the other two places claimed his remains.

Having assembled at Dundurn for the funeral
they carried the coffin containing his body through
Glen Ogle until they reached the point where the

road branched, one road leading to Killin and the other to Strathfillan.

Here the procession halted; the coffin was put down and soon a violent dispute arose as to which road should be taken.

Swords were drawn, and blood flowed freely; then it was observed that where one coffin had been put down, two exactly alike were now lying!

That settled the dispute! Each of the contending parties seized a coffin and marched to the burying-place of its choice. So it can never be known whether Strathfillan or Killin has the saintly relics; whether each has a whole body, or whether, in his desire to promote peace, St. Fillan divided his body between them!

From earliest days Crieff was the seat of the courts of the Stewards of Strathearn. These courts were held about half a mile from Crieff in the open air on a circular piece of ground, which was surrounded by a low wall of earth and stones.

It belonged to MacLaurin of Broich.

In the centre of this ground stood a blasted tree, and many a poor, terrified wretch was accused, tried, and condemned on this dread spot. The Highlanders, it is said, used to touch their bonnets as they passed it and say, " God bless her nainsel and the Tiel tamn you ! "

From various causes the MacLarens as time went on declined in strength and importance. Three branches of the family—Maurice of Tiree, Conan of Balquhidder, and Laurin of Ardveche—signed the Ragman Roll in 1296, swearing fealty to Edward I of England.

Among those who signed along with the MacLarens and the rest was Robert Bruce, the man who was, in the end, to free Scotland from the English oppression. When that time came and the Battle of Bannockburn rid Scotland of the " Proud Usurper " the MacLarens were there, and fought with a will.

Like all other Scottish land-owning families they were obliged to sign, or be deprived of their lands. The list of names on the Ragman Roll was put into book form which can still be seen in the Tower of London, though the original documents have crumbled actually to rags.

Certain privileges had descended to them, and in their pride of race the Clan was careful to insist on the observance of these.

To seat themselves in the Kirk of Balquhidder before any belonging to other Clans dare cross its threshold, was deemed by them their peculiar privilege, and, needless to say, their insistence on this particular right led to quarrels, which sometimes developed into unseemly brawls, even at the very door of the church. Things came to a head when Sir John MacLaren, the Vicar of the Church, was killed in one of these fights ; and it led to several of his kinsmen being prosecuted and outlawed.

The MacLarens were always on the look-out for slights or insults—partly because they had on each side of them a powerful rival Clan.

On one side were the MacGregors, who never let the MacLarens forget that *they* claimed descent from Kenneth Alpin—the King who had granted the MacLarens their lands—and on the other side were the Buchanans of Leny.

Fierce conflict arose between the MacLarens and the Buchanans because a Buchanan—whether by intention or not—struck a MacLaren on the cheek with a salmon which he was carrying and knocked off his bonnet! An annual fair to which the whole countryside turned out took place at Kilmahog about the time and when this MacLaren told his clansmen there about the insult that he had received, the Fiery Cross went round the Clan at once.

The Buchanans, anticipating this, advanced upon the MacLarens before the Clan had had time to assemble, and at first they drove them back.

But one clansman—after seeing his son cut down by the enemy—suddenly " saw red," and turned on the Buchanans with devastating fury, shouting the war-cry of the Clan, " Craig Tuirc! Craig Tuirc ! "

His clansmen rallied and caught the fever of battle from him, and the Buchanans were slain in great numbers and driven over a fall in the Balvaig stream which is known by the name of " Linan

an Seicachan " (" The Cascade of the Dead Bodies ").
Only two Buchanans escaped from the field.

Between the MacLarens and the MacGregors there
existed a chronic and deadly enmity which led, in the
sixteenth century, to a shocking outrage by the
MacGregors.

They came in great strength and fell on eighteen
householders of the name of MacLaren, killing them
and their families and taking possession of their
lands. The law was surely a very slow-moving
instrument in those days, for forty-six years passed
before the MacGregors were brought to trial and
outlawed for the offence—which was described in
the indictment as " the crewall murthour and
burning of auchtene houshalders of the Clan Lawren,
thair wyves and bairns, committit fourtie sax yeir
syne or thairby."

Inver--nenty was one of the properties which the
MacGregors took ; and they kept possession of it
for nearly two hundred years.

A romantic happening in the MacLaren history
was an alliance which they made with the Stewarts of
Appin. One of the Stewarts of Lorn had fallen in
love at first sight with a beautiful daughter of Mac-
Laren of Ardveche. They had a son called Dugald,
and, so that he might inherit, Stewart arranged,
on his wife's death, to marry Mary MacLaren in the
Chapel of Dunstaffnage. This did not suit the
Campbells at all. Two of them were married to

Stewart sisters and they had expected to be able to claim Lorn for them.

They tried to prevent the marriage by getting Stewart assassinated in the chapel, but, although he died of his wounds, he was able to go through with the ceremony first, and so legalise his son. In spite of this the Campbells seized the Lordship of Lorn and most of the lands ; but in the end Dugald Stewart got back his inheritance and he was Chief of the Clan for thirty years.

When the Rebellion of the " 'Forty-five " came, the MacLarens, loyal to Prince Charlie, came out on his side and fought, some of them under the Murrays of Atholl, but most of them under Stewart of Ardshiel.

By this time there was again a MacLaren at Invernenty and he joined his Clan and fought at Culloden, being taken prisoner after the battle.

Along with other prisoners he was being taken to Carlisle by an escort of soldiers, from whom he escaped in a most sensational way.

There is a very deep and gloomy hollow in the hills near Moffat, high above which the main road from Edinburgh to Moffat passes.

Even on a fine day its depth and aloofness make it an impressive place, while on a dull day it is positively awe-inspiring.

It goes by the name of the " Devil's Beef Tub "— or sometimes " Johnstone's Beef Tub."

It takes its name from cattle-rievers of olden days, who used it as a keeping-place for stolen cattle.

Once driven into the hollow cattle were easily guarded. They could not stray up the steep sides of the hollow and one or two men could watch the entrance to the basin while their companions " scouted."

The morning on which young MacLaren passed along the high road to Moffat with the other prisoners was a dull and misty one.

He was a resourceful lad and he knew the Beef Tub. Keeping on the side of the road nearest the hollow, at a suitable moment he slipped over the steep edge, rolling down and down into the basin ; and he rightly judged that the soldiers, who did not know the place, would scarcely dare to launch themselves after him into that gloomy and mist-filled pit.

They waited for some time and the mist cleared, but no MacLaren was to be seen away down on the bottom of the basin. And yet he was there all the time, and literally under their noses !

When he rolled down to the bottom he knew that cover must be found or he would certainly be shot from above. So when he came upon a bog hole he was glad to let himself sink into it right up to the neck. Then he dug out a piece of turf from a tussock close by and he placed it upon his head. No wonder the soldiers could see nothing of Mac-

Laren! There he remained all day, terrified to move, until darkness brought him liberty.

Then he made his escape, and, walking by night, he made his way in time to Balquhidder.

When he reached Invernenty he disguised himself as a woman, and in woman's dress he remained undiscovered until 1747, when all danger was over.

One of the most famous mathematicians of the eighteenth century was Colin MacLaurin, the son of an Argyll minister. He was Professor of Mathematics, first at Aberdeen University, and afterwards at Edinburgh University. He was not a Jacobite, for when Prince Charlie was marching on Edinburgh in 1745 he organised the defence of the city; and he assembled some three hundred citizens in the college yard and superintended the serving out of arms to them.

It was a useless precaution, as it turned out, for the advance guard of the Prince got possession of one of the city forts, and after a mild resistance Edinburgh surrendered—although the Castle, which was strongly garrisoned, did not. Professor MacLaurin withdrew to England, but the exposure and the fatigue brought on an illness to which he succumbed.

His son was a famous advocate and became a Lord of Session with the title of Lord Dreghorn. He it was who claimed the Chiefship of the Clan in 1781.

Nearer our own days it must not be forgotten that it was a MacLaren who, in 1817, established that great Scottish newspaper, the *Scotsman*, which was edited by himself for over a quarter of a century.

XIX

CLAN GRAHAM

IT is about nineteen hundred years since the Romans came to Britain and took possession of all the flat part of England and part of the south of Scotland.

They planned to conquer the Highlands also but the Highlanders offered determined opposition to that. They considered that a supply of food for their soldiers would be very hard to get in such rocky country, so they contented themselves and built a long wall from the Firth of Forth to the Firth of Clyde. They made watch-towers along the wall and established camps at intervals, to make certain that if they could not get into the Highlands, neither should the inhabitants get out ! This did not please the Highlanders at all. The country from which the wall excluded them was fine rich land, just as useful to them as it was to the Romans. Some day, they determined, all that would be changed.

At last, early in the fifth century, the clansmen assembled in great numbers, made a determined attack upon the wall and managed to breach it. And the first man to get over the wall was a Graham !

There is a rival explanation. It is that the name Grahame or Grime is taken from the Norse word " Grimr "—meaning Devil—and that the wall was called Grime's or Devil's Dyke because people thought it was too wonderful to have been made by the hands of men.

Whatever truth there is in the story, the remaining part of the wall is still called Graham's Dyke, and appears under this name in the old maps.

There are very few families, Sir Walter Scott says, which can boast of historical renown such as that of the Grahams.

The name occurred in records in the twelfth century, when William of Graham was granted the lands of Abercorn and Dalkeith. In the following century land near Montrose was granted to his grandson by William the Lion.

One member of the Clan in the following generation married the daughter of the Earl of Strathearn and acquired lands in Perthshire where later many branches of the Clan settled. A son of this marriage, Sir John the Graham of Dundaff, was the bosom friend of Wallace. He fell at Falkirk, fighting for Scotland's freedom. His epitaph in Latin, translated, runs as follows :

" Here lys
Sir John the Graeme, baith wight and wise,
Ane of the Chiefs reskewit Scotland thrice ;
Ane better knight not to the world was lent
Nor was gude Graham of truth and hardiment—"

and that is a pretty good description of many a Graham warrior since the time of Sir John the Graeme !

The family exchanged with Robert the Bruce the property of Cardross in Dumbartonshire, for Old Montrose in Forfarshire, from which they afterwards took their titles of nobility.

The marriage of a Graham clansman with the daughter of Robert III brought royal blood into the family, and the great-great-grandson of this pair became Earl of Montrose in recognition of his prowess at the Battle of Sauchieburn.

Four generations more and we come to James Graham, the fifth Earl, whose name has been handed down to posterity as " The Great Montrose."

He was one of the most prominent of the nobles who helped Scots people to resist the compulsion of Charles I in making their form of worship that of the Episcopal Church ; and he assisted at the signing of the Covenant which was drawn up to defend their faith and preserve their religious freedom.

When an army was raised to support the Covenanters' cause Montrose conducted its successful campaign in Aberdeenshire and defeated Viscount Aboyne at Bridge of Dee.

Afterwards, for some reason, he became a convert to the Royalist side. He was created a marquis, and became lieutenant-general of the King's Forces in Scotland.

The leader in many a skirmish, he won several pitched battles for the Crown, and being a man of extraordinary resource and courage, he could inspire his army to great deeds.

At the Battle of Kilsyth, for instance, his men found themselves opposed for the first time by a regiment of cuirassiers, the sight of whose glittering armour seemed to strike terror to the hearts of Montrose's soldiers.

Montrose heard mutterings that it would be useless to try and fight men clad in iron, and he saw that the situation must be dealt with, or disaster would surely overtake him.

So he set himself to turn this ugly feeling of doubt into one of contempt ; so riding up to the head of his cavalry and pointing to the cuirassiers, he addressed his men :

" Gentlemen, these are the men you beat at Alford, the men who ran away from you at Auldearn and Tippermuir. They are such cowards that their officers could not induce them to face you unless they were protected by armour ! To show our contempt we'll fight them *in our shirts* ! " And with that he threw off his coat and waistcoat before them all. The effect was instantaneous.

His example was followed with the utmost enthusiasm by the whole army.

The day being very sultry, the physical relief from heavy uniforms helped the general feeling of upliftment. Montrose knew that, although there was stiff work to be got through first, the spirit of the men would help towards victory—and his faith was justified.

His next orders were that he should take his army to the Borders and get on the track of General Leslie's army—but now trouble began to brew. The Highlanders did not want to spend another winter away from their homes, and they withdrew— only for a time, they said.

The Earl of Aboyne and his countrymen were the next to forsake him, and he was left with a sadly reduced army. Then, before he could make up the numbers, he had to face the Battle of Philiphaugh, which was a complete disaster—and he had to flee to Norway.

Five years later, at the command of Charles II, he

M

landed in Caithness with a small army and marched into Sutherland. And there at Carbisdale on the Kyle of Sutherland the military career of the Great Montrose ended.

After being a fugitive for four days he was captured by Macleod of Assynt and handed over to the Covenanters ; and as a writer has described it—" a life of meteoric splendour " closed on the gallows in the Grassmarket of Edinburgh. The great-grandson of the famous Earl—a very distinguished descendant—was the first Duke of Montrose.

A branch of the Clan which was closely identified with the Great Montrose was that of his cousin, Graham of Inchbrakie. When Montrose came in disguise from England to arrange about the Royalist rising, Inchbrakie received him at his House of Tullibelton, where in the park was a great yew tree whose foliage sheltered him from prying eyes on more than one occasion. When he raised the Stewart Standard at Blair Atholl, Inchbrakie was with him and was one of his chief officers during the campaign ; but the Commonwealth soldiers when they came to Scotland made him suffer for his Royalism, for they burned down his castle and threw him into prison.

This Graham was the Laird to whose family a witch, named Kate McNiven, guaranteed perpetual possession of the estate of Inchbrakie. Kate was nurse to the Laird's little son and, although she was young, she was already learned in the black art of witchcraft.

She had an idea that the boy would bring her bad luck or even death, and she brooded over that idea until at last she tried to poison him. The boy disliked her as much as she disliked him, and she was eventually relieved of her duties.

Although she was branded as a sorceress it did not affect the kindliness of her old master towards her. But she played tricks on him all the same.

In those days when people went to any public function they took their own knives and forks with them !

One day Inchbrakie went to a festival at Dunning, and as usual he carried his knife and fork in his pocket and put them on the dinner-table.

He was much bothered by a bumble bee which buzzed round his head at dinner and would not give him peace to eat. So he got up at last and chased it out of the window.

When he went back to his place at the table his knife and fork were nowhere to be seen, and, search as he liked—over the table and under the table— he could find no trace of them. It was a humiliating position ! But when he got home his knife and fork were found in their usual place !

Of course people believed that Kate had turned herself into a bee in order to play this annoying trick !

Her evil deeds became notorious and at last evidences of her sorcery were collected and she was tried for witchcraft and condemned to be burnt.

Her old master did his best to help her, but the whole parish was against her release ; so the stake was pitched and the faggots piled on the summit of the Knock of Crieff, and Kate was dragged to the stake in the presence of a huge crowd. When she was chained to the post, her eye lighted on Inchbrakie among the crowd, and, knowing that he had been her friend she asked that she might speak with him.

As he approached, she bent her head and bit off a large blue bead from a necklace which she was wearing. Spitting it out towards him she told him to keep it as a talisman, and so long as the bead was treasured, the family of Inchbrakie should never want a lineal heir, nor lose the ancestral property.

The bead, set in a ring, was kept as an heirloom in the family. It was said to be an uncut sapphire.

A Graham warrior, celebrated both in history and song, was John Graham of Claverhouse. He was born in 1649, and was of the same family as Montrose.

A staunch Jacobite, the Covenanters looked upon him as their deadly enemy. Such was their awe of him that they declared that he was not only proof against bullets, but that the black horse on which he always rode had been given him by the Devil !

On this horse Claverhouse was said to perform the most marvellous feats, flying like a bird along the sides of precipitous hills and treading safely through pathless bogs where an ordinary horse must have come to grief.

In 1688 he was second in command of the Scottish army and was ordered south to protect the Stewart throne, and oppose the landing of William of Orange.

At that time he was created Viscount Dundee,— the " Bonnie Dundee " of the old song.

James II had fled to France, and Claverhouse coming back to Scotland, all his energy was bent on helping forward the Stewart cause.

He organised a great rising in the Highlands, where " Bonnie Dundee " was a name with a charm.

The Jacobites flocked to his standard, and, in a great battle at Killiecrankie in 1689, King William's forces under Mackay were completely routed.

But rejoicing was turned into mourning, for, at the moment of victory a bullet ended the life of the brave leader and lost to Scotland one of her most gallant soldiers.

" So, amidst the battle's thunder,
    Shot, and steel, and scorching flame,
    In the glory of his manhood
    Passed the spirit of the Graeme !

.   .   .   .

    Sleep !—and till the latest trumpet
    Wakes the dead from earth and sea ;
    Scotland shall not boast a braver
    Chieftain than our own Dundee ! "

AYTOUN.

The Border Grahames are descended from a famous swordsman, the second son of Malise, Earl of Strathearn who was called " Sir John with the Bright Sword."

To a great tilting match given near Berwick by Henry of Lancaster (afterwards Henry IV of England), twenty Scots knights, renowned as swordsmen, were invited to come and tilt with twenty English lords, and prove their skill.

One of the Border Grahames tilted with the English Baron Talbot, whose life was saved only by the breastplates he wore.

At supper an English knight challenged Grahame to tilt with him next day.

" Dost thou ask to tilt with me ? " said Grahame. " Rise early in the morning, confess your sins, and make your peace with God, for you shall sup in Paradise ! "

Next morning Graham's sword ran the Englishman through the body and he died where he fell.

The Menteith Grahams were descended from Robert II through David, Earl of Strathearn.

One of them, being vain of his descent, boasted that " he was as good as Charles I," and when the King was told he deprived him of the earldom.

A later member of the family was given the Earldom of Menteith and Airth.

The story is told that one of these Earls held a boasting match with Finlayson, the Town Clerk of Stirling.

The Earl asked the Clerk whether he had seen the sailing cherry-tree ? " No," said Finlayson, " What is that, my Lord ? " The Earl said that a goose on the Lake of Menteith had once swallowed a cherry stone, and in due time a tree grew out of her mouth and could be seen when she was swimming round the lake. At present, he said, the tree was laden with cherries of the most wonderful flavour !

He challenged his guest to tell as wonderful a story. Finlayson was not easily beaten, so he said : " Did your Lordship ever hear of the ball which was fired from one of Cromwell's cannon when he was at Airth ? " " No," said the Earl. " What is the tale ? "

" It is this," said the Clerk. " The ball fired from Airth reached Stirling Castle and lodged in the mouth of a trumpet which one of the soldiers was sounding!"

"And I suppose the trumpeter was killed?" said Lord Menteith.

"Not at all!" said Finlayson. "He blew the ball back again and killed the artilleryman who had fired it!"

After the Battle of Pinkie some Appin Stewarts on their way home called at the inn of Port of Menteith, tired, dejected and hungry.

In the inn they found a fine dinner of roasted hens which had been prepared for a marriage party of the Grahams at which the Earl of Menteith was to be a guest. The hungry Stewarts looked upon this as a veritable godsend, ate up everything and went on their way.

When the wedding party arrived and found what had happened they were naturally very wroth.

The Earl with a number of retainers pursued and fought the Stewarts, who added insult to injury by accompanying each sword-thrust with sneering references to the roasted hens. Most of the Stewarts were killed; but the origin of the quarrel earned for the Grahams the nickname of "Gramoch-an-Garrigh," which is "Graham of the Hens."

Sometime afterwards, it is said, a Graham and a MacGregor quarrelled on the Hill of Coldon beside the Lake of Menteith.

MacGregor in the height of his passion was in the

act of opening his mouth to call out " Hen Grahams ! " when, anticipating his intention, Graham drew his sword and severed the MacGregor's head from his body.

But his antagonist had the last word, for the head of the MacGregor rolled to the foot of the hill crying out " Hen Grahams ; Hen Grahams ! " all the way to the bottom !

XX

CLAN SINCLAIR

THE SINCLAIR CLAN is descended from
William, the son of the Comte de St. Clair,
a Norman noble who was related to William
the Conqueror. Having accompanied William the
Conqueror to England in 1066, he afterwards
settled in Scotland, where his descendants became
connected by marriage with many noble families
and even with Royalty.

The first St. Clair is described as a very fair
man of great stature, yellow haired and well pro-
portioned.

He was the direct ancestor of the Sinclairs, Earls
of Caithness, the St. Clairs of Roslin, the Sinclairs

of Herdmanstoun and the St. Clairs of Dysart
and Ravenscraig in Fife. There are many other
branches, all descended from the same stock,—
except the Argyllshire Sinclairs, who do not seem
to have any connection with those of the north.

A St. Clair accompanied Douglas—the " Good
Sir James " as he was called—when he carried the
heart of Robert the Bruce to be buried in the Holy
Land ; actually he played an important part in the
tragedy which befell Douglas.

Sir James sailed from Scotland to Flanders on the
first stage of his long journey to Palestine. There he
heard of a religious war against the Saracens which
was going on in Spain, and he and his companions
(one of whom was Sir William St. Clair of Roslin)
determined to take part in it before proceeding to
Jerusalem. Douglas was a seasoned warrior, the
hero of seventy battles, and his companions were a
picked company of gallant knights and soldiers.
There was no reason to fear reverse. And yet, in a
dream, Sir James was warned by a Pilgrim that he
should not live to accomplish his vow !

> " Lord James of Douglas, mark my rede
> That heart shall pass once more
> In fiery fight against the foe
> As it was wont of yore.
> And it shall pass beneath the Cross
> And save King Robert's vow ;

But other hands shall bear it back,
Not, James of Douglas, thou ! "

AYTOUN.

Their first action took place on the borders of Andalusia in Spain, where the Moors were defeated ; but after their camp had been taken, Douglas and his companions—ever daring—pursuing the Moors too far, got separated from the main Spanish army, and found themselves cut off and surrounded by Moors.

Sir James turned to cut his way through the Infidels and would probably have succeeded, but suddenly he was aware that Sir William St. Clair of Roslin was fighting desperately, with Moors all round him hacking at him with their sabres.

" See," said Douglas, " yonder worthy knight will be slain unless he have instant help ! "

With that he galloped to the rescue, but was himself surrounded and hard pressed.

Then seeing no chance of escape, Sir James took from his neck the casket containing the precious heart and addressing the casket's precious contents he said :

" Pass first in fight as thou wert wont to do. Douglas will follow thee or die ! " Then throwing the King's heart among the enemy he rushed forward to where it fell. These were the last words and deed of a heroic life, for Douglas fell, overpowered by his enemies.

Next day the body of Douglas and the casket were found in the field and were borne reverently home to Scotland by the survivors, the heart being placed in Melrose and the body of Sir James in the burial-place of his forefathers at the Parish Church of Douglas.

Another William, Earl of St. Clair, who lived a hundred years later was one of the most distinguished men of his century. When James I, who had been captured as a boy and kept for eighteen years in England, was about to be ransomed by the Scots, the Earl of St. Clair was one of the hostages sent to London as a guarantee of good faith.

Later on, when James's daughter was to be conveyed to France for her marriage with the Dauphin, the Earl (now High Admiral of Scotland) was her escort. He received the title Earl of Orkney and had to go to Norway to acknowledge his vassalage.

On his return he devoted himself to the building of castles, palaces and churches, one of which was Roslin Chapel, founded as the Collegiate Church of St. Matthew.

For that undertaking alone his memory deserves to be preserved. The Chapel is a gem of archi-tecture, remarkable for its many carvings and the beautiful " Prentice Pillar " with its romantic history. The Pillar is said to have been the work of an apprentice during the absence of his master who had gone to Rome in order to get ideas for a column which should be of surpassing beauty.

When he found on his return that the apprentice's genius had forestalled him, the architect in his jealousy seized a stone hammer, and gave the talented lad a fatal blow !

Up to the time of James VII the St. Clairs were laid in the crypt of Roslin Chapel in their complete armour, and tradition tells that on every occasion when one of the " lordly line of high St. Clair " passed away, Roslin Chapel was seen as if it were flaming to heaven.

Scott describes it in his ballad of *Rosabelle* :

" Seem'd all on fire that chapel proud
    Where Rosslyn's Chiefs uncoffined lie."

Roslin Castle dates from the twelfth century and is now in ruins, but for hundreds of years the St. Clairs lived there in great splendour. One of them became a patron of the Gipsies who, in the Middle Ages, overran the country, and were both disliked and feared by the country people because of their depredations.

It is related in an old record how Sir William St. Clair of Roslin in the seventeenth century " delivered ance ane Egyptian, ready to be stranglit from the gibbet at Burrow Mure." Perhaps the Gipsy had only stolen a hen—Gipsies were hanged for very small causes in those days! At any rate Sir William showed his pity, with the result that, for a hundred years afterwards, every May and June saw the Gipsies encamped in the neighbourhood of Roslin. In order to show their gratitude they used to entertain the St. Clairs by singing and dancing before them and by acting plays—the nature of which has not been recorded.

In July 1513 James IV issued a summons for the whole array of his kingdom to meet him in the third week of August at the Borough Muir of Edinburgh.

So, one fine Monday morning early in August the Caithness Sinclairs, many hundreds strong, went swinging along over the Ord of Caithness, clad in green uniforms—a goodly sight!—with the Earl of Caithness at their head. But alas for the Clan! There was no brave return from the bloody field of Flodden!

So many were killed that scarcely one Sinclair family of note had a male representative left; and so strong was the impression left by the event that it is said that for two centuries after, no Sinclair would dress in green or willingly cross the Ord of Caithness on a Monday!

The title "Cock of the North" which is now associated with the Gordon Clan was originally used by the Sinclairs of Caithness. It was not assumed by the Duke of Gordon until after Flodden when the Earl of Caithness and all the fighting Sinclairs were killed.

Between the two great northern Clans of Caithness and Sutherland there was always enmity and bitter jealousy, which led to shocking crimes and cruelty.

There was one terrible affair in the sixteenth century, when George, Earl of Caithness, and Isobel Sinclair (wife of one of the Gordons, whose son was next heir to the Sutherland earldom) are said to have conspired to poison the Earl of Sutherland, his Countess and their son Alexander, at a supper party at Helmsdale ! The poison—which had deadly but lingering effects—was infused in wine which the Earl and Countess drank.

When both became ill they suspected poisoning. Their son, who had been out hunting, and coming in—late for supper—was not allowed to touch food, but was instead sent home supperless to Dunrobin. The Earl and Countess were carried home the following day but they died a few days afterwards. The evidence against the Earl of Caithness was not sufficient to convict him, but Isobel Sinclair was apprehended and sent to Edinburgh to stand her trial.

She was condemned to death but she died on the morning fixed for her execution ; and her punishment was severe.

Her own son was in the house at Helmsdale when she prepared the fatal wine.

Feeling very thirsty he called for a drink, and one of the servants—all unknowing—gave him some of the poisoned wine, which he drank; and he died in agony two days afterwards—the innocent victim of his mother!

On Sinclair Bay, not far from Wick, are the ruins of two great castles,—old strongholds of the Sinclairs —named Castle Girnigoe and Castle Sinclair.

They are built on precipitous rocks, and—looked at from the sea, it is difficult to see where rock ends and castle begins! That these old abodes of the Earls of Caithness have witnessed many gruesome sights one cannot deny; although tragedies are attributed to the gloomy keeps which perhaps do not always bear the test of history.

But there is not much doubt that the story of the horrible treatment of the Master of Sinclair was founded on fact. The Earl of Caithness was displeased with his son for having given what he thought too easy terms to their opponents, the Murrays, after a raid in Dornoch.

The young man was asked to come to Girnigoe, and, once there, he was thrown into a dungeon below the castle, put in fetters, and kept a prisoner for nearly six years.

His keepers got tired of watching him and made a fiendish plan—with the consent of his inhuman parent, it is said—to hasten his death.

They gave him no food for five days, Then they

N

set before him a piece of salt beef which he ate ravenously.

But when he called for water to drink they refused to give him any, and he died of raging thirst ! Then there is a story of a dungeon below Castle Sinclair also.

In the seventeenth century a forger, named Smith, and a man who had assisted him were tried and sentenced to death in Edinburgh. The sentence was carried out in the case of the assistant, who was burned, but Smith—the real culprit—got off in a manner which would horrify present-day justice. While he was in prison he managed to get some tools belonging to his trade, and he made a lock of such ingenious device and beautiful workmanship that it had no equal anywhere. The lock was shown to the King, who was so pleased with it that he ordered Smith's execution to be delayed.

Then Lord Elphinston, the Lord Treasurer of Scotland—who said it was a pity that such a skilful workman should be deprived of life—got a fresh respite for him, and he was set free ! Smith went to Caithness where he served the Earl of Caithness for seven or eight years.

He had a workshop under the rock on which Castle Sinclair was built, and to which there was a secret passage from the Earl's bedroom. No one except the Earl was admitted to the workshop, and as the smith was often heard working during the night, the country people naturally became anxious to know what he was doing.

The mystery was revealed at last when a great deal of counterfeit money inundated Caithness !

It was traced to Smith, who was arrested in Thurso.

The Earl was away from home at the time and his relations were very indignant that any private servant of his should be interfered with—in spite of the fact that Smith's guilt was proved beyond doubt.

The arrest raised a regular tumult, in which several people, including Smith himself, were killed ; and a fresh feud was kindled between the Earl of Caithness on the one side and the Gordons and Mackays on the other.

The northern Clans were a fierce, quarrelsome lot, always ready to fly at each other on the slightest provocation. Of the four greatest tribes, Sinclair, Gordon, Mackay and Gunn, there was always at least one that—like the children—was " not play-ing " with one or more of the others !

It was all rather like the old rhyme :

" Taffy was a Welshman, Taffy was a thief,
    Taffy came to my house and stole a leg of
        beef ;
    I went to Taffy's house ; Taffy wasn't at
        home.
    Taffy came to my house and stole a marrow
        bone."

Each of these turbulent northern Clans took the rôle of Taffy at one time or another, with either land or cattle as the " bone of contention " !

In the seventeenth century, George, the sixth Earl of Caithness, who had no family, sold his lands and title to Sir John Campbell of Glenorchy, who had lent him large sums of money on his estates from time to time.

When he died Sir John took the title of Earl of Caithness. Sinclair of Keiss, the legal heir, also assumed the title of Earl of Caithness, in spite of an interdict from the Privy Council.

Glenorchy raised his Clan and marched north, meeting the Sinclairs in battle at a place called " The burn of the hawks (or thieves) " in Caithness. The Campbells were trained soldiers and the Caithness men were at a disadvantage. They were defeated and chased for two miles towards Wick, with the Campbell pipers adding insult to injury by playing a tune called :

> " The carles with the breeks, with the breeks,
> with the breeks,
> The carles with the breeks are flying before
> us ! "

an allusion to the fact that the Sinclairs wore the trews. It was a sore subject in Caithness ; until Sinclair of Keiss—who carried his claims to Parliament—was at last reinstated in both titles and estates, while Campbell, to square matters, was given the title of Earl of Breadalbane.

Some verses which were written on the episode begin :

" Short time Glenorchy Caithness ruled,
By every rank abhorred ;
He lost the title he usurped
Then fled across the Ord.
While Keiss, who firm upheld his claim
Against tyrannic might
Obtained the Sinclairs' coronet
Which was his own by right,
That coronet which William wore
Who loved his Clan so well
And with his brave devoted band
On fatal Flodden fell ! "

PRINCE CHARLIE'S ADVENTURES AFTER CULLODEN

FRIENDS IN NEED

I. IN THE HEBRIDES WITH DONALD MACLEOD

THE Rising of the " 'Forty-five" was the last act in the tragic drama in which the Stewart Kings, from Charles I onwards, played leading parts. The theme of the drama was the claim of the people to the right of worshipping as they wished. The Stewarts were Roman Catholics and each king in turn was determined to make all his subjects Roman Catholics also.

When James VII of Scotland and II of England succeeded Charles II, he resorted to force, oppression, and bloodshed in order to gain his own end. Scotland's sufferings merely strengthened her resistance, and at last the long-suffering people turned on James and drove him from the throne. The Protestant William of Orange (husband of James's daughter) was his successor, and Anne (another daughter of James) succeeded William. But still the people of Scotland had grievances, and discontent prevailed.

When Anne died and George I came to rule Britain matters came to a head. George was a Hanoverian. The Jacobites called him " the wee wee German lairdie," and he did not even trouble to learn to speak English! So an agitation was started to bring back a Stewart to the throne of Scotland, and in 1715 the Stewart standard was raised on the braes of Mar and the " Rising of the 'Fifteen " had begun.

James VII was now dead and his son James (whom the Jacobites called James VIII and the Georgians " The Pretender ") came over from France to join his supporters. But things went wrong ; he had delayed too long in coming and he found the Rising fizzling out. So—not very reluctantly—he returned to France. And it was not until his son Charles was grown up that the last desperate attempt was made to recover the Crown of Scotland for the Stewarts. Charles landed on the west coast of Scotland in July 1745, and within a month he had raised his standard at Glenfinnan. At first all went well. Everyone with whom he came into contact yielded to his charm. He was " King o' the Hieland hearts, bonnie Prince Charlie ! " With his army he marched to Edinburgh, fought and won the Battle of Prestonpans, and marched on into England, expecting people to flock to his standard. But England was lukewarm and gave him little support. Finding at Derby that the royal troops were gathering against him, he had to retreat to Scotland. At Falkirk he met and defeated a royal army under General Hawley. By this time the Highland troops were discontented and insisted on returning to the Highlands. So, much against his will, Charles made for Inverness, which town he easily took, holding it for two months. On 16th April 1746 the Jacobites met the Duke of Cumberland's army at Culloden Moor. Complete disaster was the result ; they were outnumbered and cut to pieces. The Prince and the remnant of his army took to flight and became fugitives among the hills. Some of them were captured and were imprisoned in the Tower of London ; some were beheaded ! Others managed to make their way to France, where they were a prey to constant anxiety as to the fate of their wives and families. They dared not return to Scotland. Their estates had been seized by the Crown, and they themselves were liable to death if they were caught, for they had been proclaimed outlaws. A very large sum of money was offered by Government to anyone who would give away the secret of Prince Charlie's hiding-place. But, poor as most of them were, not one of his supporters would stoop to betray him ; and in the end, accompanied by some of his friends, he got safely away to France.

Before that happened, however, they met with most amazing adventures, and had many thrilling escapes from capture. Twelve days after the Battle of Culloden the Prince and four of his friends reached the west coast of Scotland. There they met one who was to prove himself a real friend in need. He was Donald, one of the Clan Macleod, a Clan which for the most part was faithful to the Prince.

Donald Macleod was an experienced boatman, and he acted as the Prince's pilot during his adventures in the Outer Isles. Charles and his small party embarked in an eight-oared boat for the Hebrides, where he hoped to be able to charter a boat large enough to reach France. Four pecks of oatmeal was all that they could get by way of provisions, and Macleod thoughtfully put an iron pot in the boat ! It was late evening when they sailed. The weather was very threatening, but in spite of warnings from Macleod and his boatmen Prince Charlie insisted on setting out.

The boat was not far from land when a terrific storm arose. The night was black as ink, except when vivid lightning lit up the mountainous seas. Thunder crashed, and rain fell in torrents, drenching to the skin the occupants of the open boat. They had no compass by which to steer, and they were in terror of being driven on the coast of Skye, where they knew that a number of soldiers were hunting for the Prince.

At daybreak, they found themselves (to their relief) off the Island of Benbecula. There they landed, and made a fire to warm themselves and dry their clothes. From one of the islanders Prince Charlie bought a cow, and on her flesh and the meal which they had in the boat they lived for several days.

All they found for sleeping-place was the floor of an empty hut, with a sail as blanket.

They aimed at reaching Stornoway, with a view to chartering there the larger boat which they needed, and, as soon as they could, they set out. Again Fate was unkind to them, and another gale forced them to put to land—this time on a small island near Harris—with their boat damaged. They passed themselves off to the crofter on the island as shipwrecked merchants from Orkney, and he was very kind to them, and lent them another boat in which to try to get to Stornoway. Once more they encountered gales, but they did land on the main island of Lewis, though a long way from Stornoway. They tried to reach the town on foot, but they lost their way, and spent a dark and rainy night wandering about on a bleak and trackless waste of bog, cold, hungry and miserable !

As things turned out, it was well that the Prince had not gone on, for the Stornoway people had been told that he was coming, with five hundred men, to take the town ; and that he would probably burn it and seize all their cattle.

And when Macleod went on to see how the land lay, he was amazed to find a force of two hundred men gathered in Stornoway, all prepared to withstand an invasion ! Macleod was known to be a friend of the Prince, and reproaches were heaped on him for bringing Charles there. He could scarcely get them to believe that the Prince's whole following consisted of a few men ! When the Lewis men were at last convinced, they said that they had no desire to hurt Prince Charlie, but that he *must* get out of their island at once ! So Macleod had to go back with the bad news, and at daybreak next morning the little party set sail once more. They had not gone far when they saw two large vessels sailing towards them, and again they put into a little island. The fisherfolk who lived on the island thought that the Prince's boat was a press-boat, come from one of the ships of war, to compel the island men to join the Navy. So they ran away to hide, leaving the fish, which had been caught that morning, lying on the rocks. Needless to say, a fire was quickly made and the fish cooked, and a very welcome breakfast it was for Charles and his companions !

They stayed on this island for four days in a wretched hut like a pig-sty. They had to spread their sails over the roof to keep out the rain, and they lay on the bare earth floor, each keeping watch in turn. They had scarcely any food and no dry clothing, and were in a miserable plight. When they did set out again they were pursued first by one and then by another war-vessel, but they managed to reach Benbecula again without being captured. It was low water when they landed, and one of the boatmen who went to hunt for shellfish for the starving party found a large crab, which he held out to the Prince with great delight. Charles took up a pail which lay in the boat and went to the spot, and between them the pail was soon filled with crabs. So pleased was the Prince that he would not part with the pail, and in great spirits carried it for nearly two miles, until they reached a hut in which they might eat the crabs in safety. The door of the hut was so low that they had to crawl in on hands and knees, but no food cooked in a king's kitchen could have tasted better than those island crabs !

So their hardships and adventures went on, and they spent week after week in much the same way, sometimes in moderate comfort, and again in dire distress.

At last, when he was in the island of South Uist, word was brought to the Prince that a body of five hundred regular soldiers and militia had landed, only a mile and a half away ! When he heard this, Charles decided that the time had come to break up his party ; so, leaving three of his friends and the boatmen to shift for themselves, he and one other went off to the hills, carrying only two shirts with them. One of the three men left behind was the faithful Donald Macleod, who wept bitterly when he parted with the young Prince, whom he had served so well. He was taken prisoner a few days later, and was examined by General Campbell in the cabin of the warship the *Furnace*. The General asked him if he had been along with the Pretender ? " Yes," said Donald, " I *was* along with that young gentleman, and I winna deny it." " Do you know," said the General, " what money was upon that gentleman's head ? No less a sum than thirty thousand pounds, which would have made you and your family happy for ever ! " " What then ? " replied Donald. " What though I had gotten it ? Could I have enjoyed it for two days ? No ! though I could have gotten all England and Scotland for my pains, I would not have allowed a hair of his head to be touched if I could hinder it—for did he not throw himself on my care ? " At which the General said that he really could not blame him !

Macleod was sent to London, and imprisoned,

but he was released in 1747. He reached Edinburgh without a penny to carry him on to the north, but money was collected by a Leith clergyman, which enabled him to travel to his home. In admiration of his fidelity, a London gentleman presented him with a large silver snuff-box. Upon its lid was engraved an eight-oared boat, with Donald at the helm, and great waves rising all around. Macleod never put any snuff in this box, and, when asked " Why ? " he exclaimed, " Sneeshin in that box ! Na ! the deil a pickle sneeshin will ever go into it till the Stuart King be restored ! And then I'll go to London and I will put sneeshin in the box ; I will go to the Prince and say—' Sir, will you take the first sneeshin out o' my box ? ' " But that proud day never dawned, and he never saw the Prince again. It was left to a woman to rescue Charles from Benbecula and to bear him company " over the sea to Skye ! " where another chapter of his adventures opened.

PRINCE CHARLIE'S ADVENTURES AFTER CULLODEN

FRIENDS IN NEED

II. TO SKYE; WITH FLORA MACDONALD

WHEN Prince Charlie had said good-bye to his good friend, Donald Macleod, on South Uist, he had with him only Neil MacEachan—one of the Macdonald kindred. Their hope was that somehow or other they would manage to reach Skye; but now that they no longer had a boat, and that the sea was patrolled by ships of war, day and night, it almost seemed that their hope was vain. But just when the Prince's prospects appeared to be at their darkest, he made the acquaint-

ance of a young girl called Flora Macdonald, who
belonged to South Uist. Full of pity for Charles's
desperate condition she offered to help him to cross
to Skye, where she knew that friends were waiting
and anxious to assist him. But the question was—
" How to get him there ? " There were parties of
soldiers roaming over the Island of South Uist
where Charles then was ; no person was allowed
to leave without a passport ; and, as a guard was
posted at every ferry, and in the Channel between
Uist and Skye were a number of ships of war, it
seemed a desperate undertaking.

Flora's first move in the game was made when she
got herself arrested for attempting to cross one of
the ferries without a passport. She was brought
before the officer commanding the militia, and he,
very luckily for her, happened to be her own stepfather, Captain Hugh Macdonald. From him she
begged for passports which would allow her, with
an escort of her own Clan, Neil MacEachan, in
attendance, to go to her mother, who was then in
Skye. She also said that she had discovered in Uist
a maid who was a good spinner, and, as her mother
wanted a spinner just then, she thought it would be
a good idea to take this girl with her. In those days
people spun all their linen and woollen cloth at
home, from native flax and wool.

Captain Macdonald quite willingly gave her the
three passports—for herself, Neil MacEachan, and

the maid—who was described as "Betty Burke, an Irish girl and a spinner." Having got the passports Flora sent a message to Prince Charles—"All is well"—and on receipt of this he arranged with some trusted friends to row him at nightfall over to Benbecula, the nearest island. There, Flora had engaged a six-oared boat to take the party to Skye.

She and the other ladies went to the place in Benbecula where the Prince was hiding. They found him in a wretched hut standing over a fire roasting some scraps of meat for his dinner. After dinner he put on the feminine garments which the ladies had brought with them, garments which transformed him into "Betty Burke," the new maid!

The dress was of flowered linen, with a quilted petticoat, a white apron, and a brownish cloak, made with a hood in the Irish fashion.

They set out at night on the 28th of June, and when the boat left Benbecula the evening was fair and serene. But, as they rowed out to open sea, the sky began to lower, the wind rose, and the sea became so rough as to threaten them with destruction. Flora and the boatmen became very much alarmed for Charles's sake, but he did his best to cheer their spirits by telling stories and singing songs. Having no compass they had just to let the boat go as the wind would take it, and at daybreak they found themselves off the west coast of Skye. There they were hailed by a party of soldiers who called to

o

them to land. Taking no notice they continued their course northwards, but they rowed *very* slowly in hopes of quieting suspicion.

The soldiers now began to fire on them; the bullets were falling all around them and the Prince begged Flora to lie in the bottom of the boat lest she might be hit. But Flora declared that she would *never* so far disgrace herself as to look to her own safety while the Prince's life was in danger! Eventually the boatmen induced both of them to take shelter in the bottom of the boat until they were out of range of the bullets. The party landed on the north coast of Skye where they were met by Macdonald of Kingsburgh, factor to a Skye proprietor. On foot the Prince and Macdonald set out for Kingsburgh, while Flora went to visit her kinswoman. A maid in this house who had seen the Prince was very inquisitive about the " strange woman." She said to Flora that she had " never seen such an impudent-looking woman, and that she was surely either an Irishwoman or a man dressed in woman's clothes ! " When Flora told her that the stranger was an Irishwoman, the maid exclaimed, " Bless me, then ! What long steps the jade takes ; and how awkwardly she manages her petticoats ! " Which remark made Flora very uneasy about the success of the Prince's disguise.

It was late before Charles and Macdonald reached Kingsburgh. Mrs. Macdonald was roused from sleep and told to come downstairs, because her husband had come home with guests, for whom supper was wanted. Very unwillingly she dressed and came down. Her daughter met her in great alarm, saying that her father had brought home " an odd, muckle, ill-shapen wife " with him, who was walking up and down the hall with great strides ! When Mrs. Macdonald went into the hall the Prince greeted her after the fashion of the day—with a kiss, and you can guess how much startled she was to be kissed by a woman with a rough and hairy chin ! Affronted and frightened she drew her husband aside to ask him who on earth this person was ? Smiling at her, Kingsburgh said, " My dear, the person in the hall is the Prince himself." " The Prince ! " she exclaimed, " then we are all ruined, and we shall all be hanged now ! " " Hoot ! " said Kingsburgh, " we can die but once and, if we are hanged for this, we shall die in a good cause ! But go," he continued, " make haste with supper ; bring us eggs, butter, cheese and anything else handy." " Eggs, butter, cheese ! " said Mrs. Macdonald, " what supper is *that* for a Prince ? " " Oh wife," said Kingsburgh, " you little know how this good Prince has lived of late ; this will be a feast to him ! Besides, to make a formal supper would make the servants suspicious. The less ceremony the better. Make haste ; and come yourself to supper." Mrs. Macdonald, very doubtful of conducting herself properly before Royalty, said, "*I* come to supper! I know not how to behave before Majesty!" "You must come," her husband said, "the Prince will not sup unless you are present."

At supper she was placed on Charles's left hand while Flora Macdonald sat on his right. This was an honour which the Prince always gave his young protectress; and whenever she came into a room where he was sitting he always rose up on her entry. After the Prince had retired, Flora gave Kingsburgh and his lady an account of their adventures, and took counsel with them as to the future movements of Prince Charles.

It was decided that, now that "Betty Burke" had served her purpose, she should cease to exist after the following day. So next morning saw Charles don for the last time the disguise which had served him so well. The ladies helped him to fix his apron, and, just as the cap was about to be pinned on, Mrs. Macdonald asked Flora (in Gaelic) to request Charles for a lock of his hair. Flora declined to do so, but suggested that Mrs. Macdonald ask it for herself. Charles wished to know what they were talking about and, when Mrs. Macdonald explained, he laid his head on Flora's lap and told her to cut a lock! This Flora did, and the lock of hair was divided between them and was ever afterward regarded as their most treasured relic.

Mrs. Macdonald carried her homage further, for,

when Charles left the house, she went to the room in which the Prince had slept, and, folding the sheets on which he had lain, she put them carefully away, declaring that never should they be used again, except as her own winding-sheet!

The Prince and Kingsburgh left the house, and in a wood not far away the " Betty Burke " clothes were discarded for good, Charles putting on in place of them a tartan coat and waistcoat, kilt and hose, a plaid, and a wig and bonnet belonging to Kingsburgh, and so becoming, for a time at any rate, a complete Macdonald! He gave a sorrowful good-bye to Flora Macdonald, the kind-hearted girl, who at peril of her own life had watched over him with the utmost care and affection, and had rescued him from unbelievable dangers. In his further wanderings he assumed many other disguises, but none so daring nor so romantic as that of the Irish spinner, " Betty Burke."

PRINCE CHARLIE'S ADVENTURES AFTER CULLODEN

FRIENDS IN NEED

III. THE MAINLAND—
WITH MACKINNONS, MACDONALDS, CAMERONS, THE MEN
OF GLENMORISTON AND CLUNY MACPHERSON

PRINCE CHARLIE after he had wandered in Skye for some time saw that there was no hope of escaping from the island to France. It would be impossible to avoid the ships of war which continually watched its shores; and the island itself was policed by Militia. So his only hope seemed to lie in the mainland, and, with Malcolm Macleod (a youth of good family) as his companion, he started on a new series of adventures.

When he left Kingsburgh House all that he had in the world besides the clothes in which he stood up was a package containing four shirts, a cold fowl, some sugar and a bottle of brandy ! Pretending to be Macleod's servant; and, with a bag thrown over his shoulder, he walked behind his supposed master, like a gillie or footman, and when spoken to touched his bonnet respectfully !

When they came to a part of the country which was known to be hostile, he tore the ruffles from his shirt and removing his buckles tied up his shoes with string. Binding his brow with a napkin, he pretended that his head was hurt ; and in this guise he reached the friendly country of the MacKinnons, who hid him in a cave on the seashore, while they made arrangements for a boat to take him to the mainland.

On a July night he reached Moidart on the west coast of Scotland, with two of the MacKinnons,— one of them the old Chieftain of the Clan. There he lay low for a few days.

On the fourth day he had a very narrow escape from capture. The MacKinnons thought that they might venture to row along the shore of Loch Nevis. Charles was in the bottom of the boat, and luckily they had thrown a plaid over him, for in turning a point, they came unexpectedly on a boat tied to a rock, and so close that their oars almost touched it. In this boat were a party of Militia who called to them to come ashore. Needless to say the MacKinnons did *not* obey! They rowed off as fast as they could, with the Militia in hot pursuit. At a point where a wood hid their boat for a moment or two, Prince Charlie sprang ashore and escaped among the dark trees where he hid, and afterwards at night-time was able to rejoin his friends.

They were now in the Macdonald country, which marched with that of the Camerons. The Macdonalds had promised to place the Prince under the protection of Lochiel, and he and his clansmen were, in their turn, to guide him to MacPherson territory. The MacPherson chief—" Cluny " as he was called —was prepared to hide him until a safe passage to France could be assured.

But a rumour had got about that Charles was hiding near Borodale, and such precautions were taken by the military authorities to prevent his escape that it seemed that only a miracle could save him ! A chain of posts was formed across the heads of the sea lochs, so as to intercept him if he should try to escape into the interior. To catch him, should he try to get off by sea, cruisers and boats were stationed at the mouths of the lochs. Along a thirty-mile line sentinels were placed, so near to each other, that in the daytime, no one could possibly pass without being seen. And at night-time great fires were lighted at every post, and the sentinels passed and repassed each other from fire to fire.

To get through such a chain seemed impossible; but the English officers made *one* mistake—and that gave Charles a loophole for escape. This mistake consisted in the fact that, after the sentinels met, they *passed each other*, so that, for a short distance, their backs were turned to each other! This offered just a chance to slip through the line— while the sentinels were walking in opposite directions! And the Prince's friends started to calculate where this chance might most safely be taken. After several days and nights of spying out the land, and getting so near to the soldiers that they could even hear them talking, a plan was decided on. So one morning at two o'clock, Cameron of Glenpean, who knew every foot of that country, led the small party to the bed of a stream, up which they crept on hands and knees towards the posts. The banks of the burn screened them from the glare of the fires, and they lay in the water—scarcely daring to breathe —while the sentries met on a plank-bridge above them! The sentries met, and passed on—now back to back! Stealthily Prince Charlie and his followers crept, inch by inch, along the bed of the burn, until they knew that there was no longer any chance of being seen. Then, gasping and utterly exhausted, they lay for ten minutes on the heather, soaked to the skin, chilled to the bone, *but free men*!

A report about French vessels being on the coast of Ross-shire sent the party northwards. The vessels when they arrived at Kintail had gone, so they made for Glenmoriston in Inverness-shire, where they had another curious experience. On the Braes of Glenmoriston they spent several days in a robbers' cave.

The robbers were seven men who, after fighting in the Rising, had been outlawed. Relying on the old saying, " Union is Strength," they formed themselves into a marauding band and terrified the country people of the district by their lawless deeds, and their disregard of property and even of human life. They took up their abode in a romantic cave on the side of a mountain, and when the Prince and his friends reached the cave, the robbers had just cooked a sheep which they had stolen, and they were about to eat their dinner. The outlawed men greeted the newcomers suspiciously, but whenever they saw the Prince they recognised him and fell on their knees and offered him their hospitality. Charles had not tasted food for two days, but he and his friends soon made amends for that omission. After dinner a bed of ferns and heather tops was made for him and he was lulled to sleep by the murmur of a burn which ran through the cave.

The Prince's clothes at this time were nearly worn out, and his tattered shoes would scarcely stay on his feet. The robbers had no change of dress to

THEY CREPT ON HANDS AND KNEES

offer their guest, but they supplied his wants in this way. Hearing that a detachment of Government troops was marching to Strathglass, they made a point of being where they could see without being seen. The troops passed, and a little way after, came some officers' servants with the personal baggage. The Highlanders fired at the servants, who, in their fright, dropped the baggage and made for shelter. The robbers coolly carried off several portmanteaux and in them found everything that Charles required! The Prince and his party next went southwards in order to visit Lochiel, who was known to be hiding in a hut on a Badenoch hill. When Charles and his friends appeared, Lochiel at first took them for enemies and ordered his men to fire on them! Luckily, just in time, he discovered his mistake, and he and Charles greeted each other affectionately. When they went into the hut, the Prince looked on such a store of good things as he had not seen for many months. Besides abundance of mutton, the hut contained a large cured ham, good dried beef sausages, and plenty of butter and cheese. Some meat was minced and cooked, and the pan was set before Charles with a silver spoon to eat with! He ate his meal with the greatest relish, exclaiming with a happy smile, " Now, gentlemen, I live like a prince ! "

His next shelter was a most unusual one. It had been prepared by Cluny MacPherson on the side of

Ben Alder, a mountain overlooking Loch Ericht. The shelter was situated within a small thick wood on the face of the mountain. To make this shelter they first laid down some rows of trees to serve for a floor ; then stakes were fixed in the earth. These stakes and the growing trees were interwoven with ropes made of heather and birch twigs to form walls, and the roof they thatched and covered with moss to make it invisible. It was held in position by a stout tree-trunk lying across the rocks, and thus it was given the name of " The Cage." Two stones formed a fireplace, and even on the brightest day smoke did not show against the grey precipice. The Cage held seven persons, four of whom—to pass the time—would be playing cards ; the fifth keeping a look-out, one baking and another firing the bread, or else cooking. But rescue was now at hand ! Early in September two French vessels arrived on the west coast, and word was brought to The Cage that these would await the Prince at Borodale. Accompanied by Lochiel and some of his friends he left at once, but they were six days in reaching the coast. On the seventh—the 20th of September 1746 —Prince Charlie, accompanied by a large number of Jacobite refugees, set sail and, after a favourable passage, reached the coast of France.

The career of " Bonnie Prince Charlie " in the home of his ancestors was now ended. Attended by only seven persons, he had landed fourteen months before on the spot from which he now departed as a fugitive, after amazing adventures, terrible sufferings, and hairbreadth escapes, lasting for five months after his defeat at Culloden. During fourteen months he won the affection and fidelity of Jacobites of all classes and, although a price of £30,000 was upon his head, no one would betray him. In all Scottish history there is not a more splendid example of devotion to an unfortunate family!

Cluny MacPherson did not accompany the Prince. For nine years he lived almost entirely in a cave near the ruins of his own house, which the King's troops had burnt to the ground.

His loyal clansmen had dug out the cave by night from the front of a precipice and had carried the stones and earth which they dug and dropped them in Loch Laggan, so that no traces would be left!

Cluny occasionally visited his friends at night and several times he narrowly escaped capture.

On one occasion he got out of the back window of a friend's house just as the King's men came in by the front door!

Another time he was too late to do even that, but he threw off his shoes, stockings and hat, " tousled " his hair and went out and held the horse of the officer who had come to search for him! He respectfully touched his forelock in acknowledgment of some money which the officer gave him when he rode off after his unsuccessful search!

Although a reward of £1000 was offered for the capture of Cluny and over a hundred people knew where he was in hiding not a whisper was allowed to escape regarding his hiding-place. At last, tired of waiting for the pardon which he had hoped for, he escaped to France, where a year later he died.